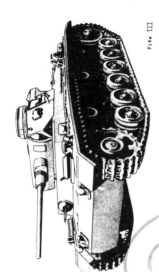

PzKw III

GERMAN AFV's

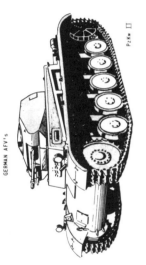

PzKw II

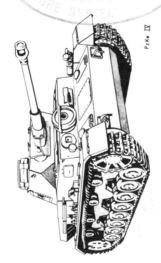

PzKw IV

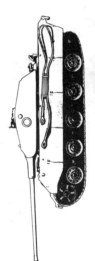

PzKw VIB "ROYAL TIGER"

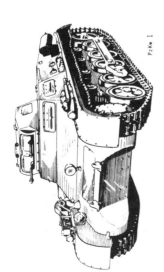

PzKw I

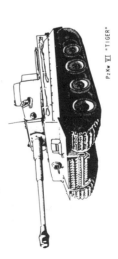

PzKw VI "TIGER"

Brassey's
Battlefield Weapons Systems
& Technology, Volume I

VEHICLES
and
BRIDGING

Brassey's
Battlefield Weapons Systems and Technology Series

General Editor: Colonel R G Lee OBE, Former Military Director of Studies at
the Royal Military College of Science, Shrivenham, UK

This new series of course manuals is written by senior lecturing staff at RMCS,
Shrivenham, one of the world's foremost institutions for military science and
its application. It provides a clear and concise survey of the complex systems
spectrum of modern ground warfare for officers-in-training and volunteer
reserves throughout the English-speaking world.

Introduction to Battlefield Weapons Systems and Technology—R G Lee

Volume I	Vehicles and Bridging—I F B Tytler *et al.*
Volume II	Guns, Mortars and Rockets—J W Ryan
Volume III	Ammunition (Including Grenades and Mines)—K J W Goad and D H J Halsey
Volume IV	Nuclear Weapons and their Effects—L W McNaught
Volume V	Small Arms and Cannons—C J Marchant Smith and P R Haslam
Volume VI	Command, Control and Communications—A M Willcox, M G Slade and P A Ramsdale
Volume VII	Surveillance and Target Acquisition—A L Rodgers *et al.*
Volume VIII	Guided Weapons (Including Light, Unguided Anti-Tank Weapons)—R G Lee *et al.*
Volume IX	Military Data Processing and Microcomputers—J W D Ward and G N Turner
Volume X	Military Ballistics—A Basic Manual—C L Farrar and D W Leeming
Volume XI	Military Helicopters—P G Harrison *et al.*

For full details of these titles in the series, please contact your local
Brassey's/Pergamon office

Other Titles of Interest from Brassey's Defence Publishers

	ier: Ski-jump to Victory
	et, 2nd Edition
	Attack: Civil Defence
	Brassey's Defence Yearbook 1985
SIMPKIN	Red Armour
SORRELS	US Cruise Missile Programs: Development, Deployment and Implications for Arms Control
WINDASS	Avoiding Nuclear War: Common Security as a Strategy for the Defence of the West

VEHICLES

and

BRIDGING

I. F. B. Tytler, N. H. Thompson, B. E. Jones, P. J. H. Wormell and C. E. S. Ryley

Royal Military College of Science, Shrivenham, U.K.

BRASSEY'S DEFENCE PUBLISHERS
a member of the Pergamon Group

LONDON · OXFORD · WASHINGTON D.C.
NEW YORK · TORONTO · SYDNEY · FRANKFURT

U.K. (Editorial)	Brassey's Defence Publishers Ltd., a member of the Pergamon Group Maxwell House, 74 Worship Street, London EC2A 2EN
(Orders and Enquiries)	Brassey's Defence Publishers Ltd., Headington Hill Hall, Oxford OX3 0BW England
U.S.A. (Editorial)	Pergamon-Brassey's International Defense Publishers, 1340 Old Chain Bridge Road, Mclean, Virginia 22101, U.S.A.
(Orders and Enquiries)	Pergamon Press Inc., Maxwell House, Fairview Park, Elmsford, New York 10523, U.S.A.
CANADA	Pergamon Press Canada Ltd., Suite 104, 150 Consumers Road, Willowdale, Ontario M2J 1P9, Canada
AUSTRALIA	Pergamon Press (Aust.) Pty. Ltd., P.O. Box 544, Potts Point, N.S.W. 2011, Australia
FEDERAL REPUBLIC OF GERMANY	Pergamon Press GmbH, Hammerweg 6, D-6242 Kronberg-Taunus, Federal Republic of Germany

First edition 1985

Library of Congress Cataloging in Publication Data
Main entry under title:
Vehicles & bridging.
(Brassey's battlefield weapons systems & technology ; v. 1)
Includes index.
1. Tanks (Military science) 2. Vehicles, Military. 3. Military bridges. I. Tytler, I. F. B. II. Series: Battlefield weapons systems & technology ; v. 1.
UG446.5.V37 1985   358'.18   84–16758

British Library Cataloguing in Publication Data

Vehicles & bridging.—(Battlefield weapons systems and technology series; v.1)
1. Armored vehicles, Military—Great Britain
I. Tytler, I.F.B. II. Series
623.74'75'0941   UG446.5
ISBN 0-08-028322-5 Hardcover
ISBN 0-08-028323-3 Flexicover

The views expressed in the book are those of the authors and not necessarily those of the Ministry of Defence of the United Kingdom.

Printed in Great Britain by A. Wheaton & Co. Ltd., Exeter

Preface

This series of books is written for those who wish to improve their knowledge of military weapons and equipment. It is equally relevant to professional soldiers, those involved in developing or producing military weapons or indeed anyone interested in the art of modern warfare.

All the texts are written in a way which assumes no mathematical knowledge and no more technical depth than would be gleaned from school days. It is intended that the books should be of particular interest to army officers who are studying for promotional examinations, furthering their knowledge at specialist arms schools or attending command and staff schools.

The authors of the books are members of the staff of the Royal Military College of Science, Shrivenham, which is comprised of a unique blend of academic and military experts. They are not only leaders in the technology of their subjects, but are aware of what the military practitioner needs to know. It is difficult to imagine any group of persons more fitted to write about the application of technology to the battlefield.

This Volume

Provides an understanding of the military vehicles required by an army and explains which type of vehicle can be provided and operated within the restraints imposed by battlefield conditions. It looks at the principles of the design of armoured vehicles and bridging in a way which does not demand a previous technical education. It is intended to be of use to army officers and anyone who has an interest in mechanised warfare.

June 1984
Geoffrey Lee

Acknowledgements

The authors wish to thank all those who have helped in their many and various ways with advice and assistance. This includes a number of Ministry of Defence (Army Department) Branches, the Royal Armoured Corps Centre and in particular the Academic Departments and Branches of the Royal Military College of Science. The co-operation and kindness of all staff at the College has been unstinting and has been a major factor in the production of this Volume.

Shrivenham
June 1984

IFBT
NHT
BEJ
PJHW
CESR

Contents

List of Illustrations

1. The Evolution of the Tank

ORIGINS

Ancient History

The concept of an "armoured" fighting vehicle does not, as many people think, start with the introduction of the tank during the 1914-18 war. History tells us that the Assyrians developed the art of mobile warfare with the use of wheeled chariots to great effect during the second millennium B.C. After their defeat by the Medes in 612 B.C. this development was continued by the Achaemenians, and many stone carvings throughout the Middle East, and particularly in the area of Ancient Persia, testify to its use not only as a weapon platform offering limited protection but also as a speedy method of transport.

The ancient chariot did not afford a great deal of protection to the rider, and any additional weight brought severe penalties in loss of mobility. With the improvement in cavalry and infantry tactics the chariot went into a decline, whilst the development of ferrous metals on a wider scale led to the introduction of effective body armour. One extreme development of this aspect was the medieval knight in armour whose personal body armour weight demanded strong but slow horses and special mounting methods which greatly reduced his mobility and effectiveness. The pendulum then swung away from increased personal protection as the greater penetrative power of firearms made it impossible to provide complete immunity from attack.

Although several machines were proposed during the Middle Ages, none really came to fruition. The most practical was the concept of Leonardo da Vinci in 1500, but this foundered on the then intractible problem of propulsion. The steam engine was able to provide a mobile power source that was utilised with notable success by the railways but its application to road movement was to prove less successful, mainly due to the relatively heavy weight of the power source and the difficulty of keeping a suitable head of steam whilst the vehicle was in motion. It was not until the latter end of the 19th century that any suitable power source became available, and with the introduction of commercially viable internal combustion engines a source of mobile and relatively lightweight power was now available.

The Need for a Tank

Initially, the internal combustion engine was regarded as only suitable to replace
the horse where hard surface roads were already in existence, and indeed the
early vehicles were so unreliable they invited rejection by the military authorities
with their instinctive distrust of innovation. By 1910 several armoured vehicles
had appeared based largely on limousine or lorry chassis. This development was
on the whole ignored by the General Staff, who were still mainly concerned with
the tactics of moving large masses of infantry and cavalry to the right place at
the right time and utilising the ever-increasing devastating power of artillery to
the best effect.

Coinciding with the introduction of armoured cars, a change was taking place on
the battlefield which was to be a major reason for the innovation of the tank as
we know it now. This was the adoption of the machine gun by most armies in the
world. Combined with a vastly improved artillery system, commanders now had
a weapon system which would give them almost complete control of the battlefield
within the field of view from their most forward defended positions. This change
in the weapon system also sounded the final death knell of the cavalry who could
not survive in such an environment.

European armies were singularly inept in learning any lessons from the American
Civil War where the slaughter reached unprecedented proportions whenever the
armies became locked in combat. Inevitably, when the great European powers
entered the arena in 1914 they were unprepared for the type of trench warfare
that emerged. After the initial manoeuvre stage the new phenomenon of control-
lable and extensive firepower forced both sides into a static trench warfare situation. The protection of the dugout matched the power of the machine gun and the
shell, with the result that mobility and the advantage of manoeuvre was lost.

Early Development

The requirement for some device to traverse the mud and shell cratered battlefield, break through the wire and overcome the obstacles of the trenches became
paramount, and in 1915 all efforts were devoted to producing such a machine. Off-
road vehicles had not received the same intensive development in Britain as they
had in the United States, where the need to travel across vast tracts of undeveloped
country and cultivate the land had inspired several versions of track-laying vehicles.
Early attempts were directed towards a "big wheel" machine, but it soon became
apparent that the sheer size of the wheel required to surmount the obstacle
envisaged would lead to a vehicle of immense size and weight with very doubtful
mobility.

Attention then focused on some form of track-laying device. "Footed" wheels such
as the Diplock wheel had achieved a brief period of popularity, but they were complex devices requiring much attention and gave only a limited advantage over a
conventional large farm tractor style wheel. Successful track-laying tractors were
now being built embodying some of the earlier pioneer work of Hornsby, who had
sold the patents to the American tractor firm of Holt's in 1912. Several lines of
enquiry were pursued, but the most likely contenders were the entirely British
"Pedrail" together with the Killen-Strait and Bullock tractors which had American
origins.

All these machines had demonstrated to a greater or lesser extent an ability to meet
the mobility requirements. The problem was now to develop what was basically
a tractor into a war machine.

Fig. 1.1 Killen-Strait tractor

The firm of Foster & Co., who were an engineering company in Lincoln, had successfully utilised the Holt track system to produce a cross-country tractor capable
of pulling several trailers across broken ground and minor obstacles. Producing
a vehicle capable of crossing a 5-ft trench would be a strong test of their engineering ability, but as they seemed to be the firm most likely to succeed, the contract
was awarded to them. The original design using a straightforward "Bullock" track
was not a success, but an improved pressed steel track showed great promise and
led to the successful prototype known as "Little Willie".

No single person can be credited with having invented the tank, or indeed having
been solely responsible for its production, but out of the mass of people who
were involved in the conception there are two names that stand out. Winston Churchill, as First Lord of the Admiralty, with his characteristic unbounding energy helped
to foster the idea, mainly, let it be said, so that the Royal Navy would man "land
ships" and so enable the Senior Service to exert some influence on the land battle.

At a later stage when the naval interest was beginning to wane, Lt Col E. D.
Swinton of the Royal Engineers, who had been pressing his ideas for some time,
gained guarded General Staff support and was able to define the military requirement more exactly and, what is more important, was able to state the requirement in a form that engineers could understand and translate into production
drawings.

At this time there were also two remarkable men at Fosters; they were William Tritton,

who was the Managing Director, and Major Walter Wilson, who was attached on special
duty from the War Office. Together they were responsible for successfully trans-
lating the military requirements into machinery. Thus they realised that although
Little Willie had demonstrated a successful system it could not meet Swinton's
demands for an 8-ft trench-crossing capability, a speed of 4 mph and an ability
to climb 5-ft parapets.

The overriding priority for the vehicle to cross an 8-ft gap and breach barbed
wire entanglements inevitably led to a reassessment, and from this came the classical
rhomboid shape of the British First World War tanks.

There was an obvious need for secrecy, and after much deliberation it was decided
that the best deception would be to call the new machines "Tanks for Mesopotamia"
and hence a new word entered into the English language.

Early Solutions

Although there was a process of continued development throughout the First World
War, the basic configuration of the British tanks remained unchanged. The early
Mark I tanks had two long 6-pounder mounted guns one on each sponson on either
side of the hull. These "long" 6-pounder guns were naval guns adapted for
military use, and although they were fairly accurate, the length of the barrel made
them cumbersome, particularly when the sponsons were removed for rail travel.
Later marks of the "Male", as the 6-pounder version was known, were fitted with
the short barrel version. The "Female" tanks were armed only with Lewis machine
guns, but as the major task of the tanks was to break through the enemy trench
lines this could be accomplished as easily by a tank with only a machine gun as
with one mounting a 6-pounder.

As we shall be concerned later with the various factors which affect the design
of a modern tank, it is worth studying some of the characteristics of the 1916 tanks.
The first thing one notices is that the track is carried along the top of the hull,
forming a complete envelope. This has two immediate effects. It means that it

Fig. 1.2 British Mark V "Male"–1917

is not possible to mount a rotating gun turret on top of the hull and that the height of the most forward part of the track was very nearly at the maximum height of the hull, which gave the vehicle a very good step-climbing ability. As the speed of the tank was only to be 5 mph, a suspension system was not essential and indeed none had been envisaged or designed. This inevitably gave the crew inside a very rough ride, which together with the heat, noise and fumes from the 150 bhp engine made life very uncomfortable. An added danger was the problem of bullet splash, as the armour protection was only boiler plate riveted onto a framework, leaving many small cracks for hot bullet fragments to find their way in. To combat this the crews had to wear protective clothing and chain-mail masks which added to their discomfort.

The propulsion train was from the engine, which was mounted centrally and just behind the driver, through a clutch to a primary gearbox and a differential and out to the steering gearboxes on either side. The drive was then transferred to sprockets by means of roller chains. The vehicle was steered, as in all track-laying vehicles, by slowing down one track and speeding up the other. In the early marks this was accomplished by giving the two steersmen signals to either change up or change down according to the direction the commander wished to go.

A major innovation on the Mark V was the introduction of epicylics into the gear train, which allowed the driver full control of the vehicle from his position in the front. It also had the important effect of freeing the commander from the more mundane tasks of controlling the vehicle and thus allowed him greater scope to exercise his command functions.

The Mark V was the most numerous tank built during the First World War and embodied the three most important characteristics of all armoured fighting vehicles; firepower, mobility and protection. These tanks were designed to overcome the siege-like conditions of the Western Front, and although they had a theoretical maximum speed of only 4 mph and a range of 40 miles, this was still a remarkable achievement for the time. Thus, when tanks were first concentrated and used *en masse* at Cambrai on the 20th of November 1917, the 474 tanks achieved a spectacular success. Unfortunately this success was not exploited, due in some part to the failure of commanders in the British Army who had forgotten the ingredients required, and in other parts to the lack of a suitable equipment to exploit success. The cavalry, who had been held in reserve to exploit the gap once it had been created, could not be risked until it was quite certain that all machine guns had been silenced. It was readily apparent that there was a need for a light fast mobile tank to penetrate rear areas after the initial break had been made. To meet this demand a Medium A or Whippet was produced in 1917 with a maximum speed of 8 mph, but initially still only with a range of 40 miles. It suffered from other serious disadvantages: the method of steering was by altering the speeds of the engines, one connected to each track, making it extremely difficult to steer a straight and steady path. The commander, with one gunner to help him, also had to serve the four machine guns in the fixed turret.

We can already see the interplay of tactics, organisations and equipment shaping the future of tank warfare. The original "Mother" was a piece of equipment designed to break the tactical stalemate imposed by the conditions of the front line. When the new equipment demonstrated that it was capable of returning mobility to the battlefield it became apparent that the organisations were unable to meet the new challenge presented. Additionally, the tactics and equipment of the cavalry, who had been kept in reserve as an exploitation force were found to be inadequate to meet the changes that mechanisation had brought to modern warfare.

The other participants in this combat had been forced into hasty development of

the tank. The Germans had produced a box-shaped vehicle on tracks which suffered from severe mobility deficiencies (see Fig. 1.3).

The French produced a similar shaped vehicle, but these also had several short-
comings and it was left to Colonel Estienne to prompt Renault to design the successful M17 light tank. This design was also adopted by the Americans in 1917, although
few ever saw active service in Europe. The Americans also became involved in
an Anglo-American project for the 38-ton British UK Mark VIII which was really
the last of the rhomboidal tanks.

DEVELOPMENT BETWEEN THE WARS

British Engineering Developments

When hostilities had ceased, the British Army was equipped with the Mark V rhomboidal tank, Whippet tanks and several variations on this theme. Colonel J. F. C.
Fuller, who had been one of the instigators of the Cambrai battle plan, had also
devised a new concept to take full advantage of the new mobility. This "Plan 1919"
was never put to the test, but had a tremendous influence on post-1918 armoured
warfare thinking and equipment. This plan depended on the ability to produce
a tank that could move at cavalry pace and had the range to achieve deep penetra-
tions.

The 1920s and 1930s led to various extremes in design, some never getting beyond

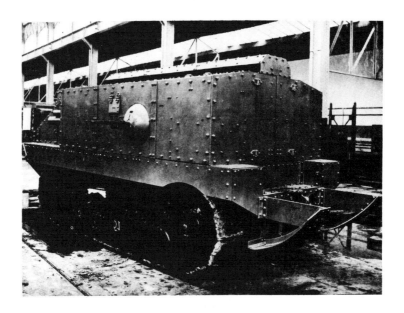

Fig. 1.3 German Schneider tank

the drawing board and few beyond the prototype stage. Some of the "heavies",
such as the Vickers Independent (29 tons) (see Fig. 1.4) in 1924, displayed several
novel features such as five rotating turrets, but proved to be frighteningly expensive in comparison with other equipments of the time.

Nevertheless, the Vickers' commercial instincts led them to search for new and
improved designs which eventually gave birth to the Vickers Medium Mark II (see
Fig. 1.5). It had several novel features, including an air-cooled engine, fully
rotating centrally located turret that housed a 47-mm gun which only fired anti-
armour projectiles and a rudimentary suspension system.

Although these vehicles never fired a round in anger, they indubitably provided,
together with the light tanks that had been developed alongside, the means to test
and try various tactics that formed the basis of the armoured battles to come.
At this time, we also saw the birth of the idea that was to dominate British tank
design philosophy for years to come. This was the belief that there was a need
for two types of tanks. A fast, highly mobile but lightly protected vehicle that
would engage other tanks on the battlefield in the same way that ships engaged
each other at sea. As its sole aim would be to destroy enemy armoured vehicles,
it was to be given only sufficient weapons for this purpose. The other type of
tank was to be a vehicle designed to accompany the infantry. Thus it needed only
to proceed at infantry pace, but should be heavily protected and its armament need
only be able to counter infantry type weapons.

United States Engineering Developments

Whilst European armies were still investigating the possibilities of light and heavy
tanks, cruiser and infantry tanks, the inventive genius of Walter Christie, an
American, was giving birth to a series of designs that were to have a profound
and lasting effect on tank design. Christie was initially concerned with producing
a vehicle that could run either on its tracks or wheels, thus avoiding the inherent
unreliability that was the bane of all tracked vehicles in those days. After several
revolutionary and experimental vehicles (including the 8.6-ton 26 mph wheeled

Fig. 1.4 A1 tank, experimental heavy "Independent", 29 tons

Fig. 1.5 A3 tank, medium Mark II, 16 tons

Fig. 1.6 Experimental Christie tank M1928, 26 mph tracks 50 mph wheels

and tracked 1928) Christie concentrated on producing a fast, reliable tracked vehicle capable of maintaining high average speeds across country.

The culmination of his designs was the M 1931 which incorporated his ideas of high power-to-weight ratio and a large wheel movement achieved by springing each wheel independently through a bell crank and coiled spring. Although the Americans purchased some of these vehicles, they never really took the design very seriously and it was the Russians who, after purchasing a pair of vehicles, really developed it into a very fine tank—the T34.

Tactical Development

It had been apparent even as early as 1917 that armoured warfare would always be unable to realise its full potential unless the problems of communications could be solved. Semaphores could help with inter-vehicle communication and pigeons could provide an unreliable and slow means of sending information back, but there was no means whereby the commander could send his orders forward once battle had been joined. By 1931, crystal controlled radios were available, giving the commander an ability to contact a large number of widely spread vehicles by voice radio. The age of mobile formations had dawned.

Inevitably there was a deep seated distrust and reluctance to accept the need for change, particularly amongst the cavalry. The feeling was probably strongest in the British Army, but it was also present in the American, French and other European armies. Another factor which delayed the acceptance of a mobile armoured warfare doctrine was what appeared to the Generals to be the extremely high cost of the equipment, which would inevitably mean an increasingly high proportion of the army equipment budget being used to finance this new arm.

By 1934 a British tank brigade had been formed, using a mixture of Vickers medium and light tanks. This brigade, together with the 7th Infantry Brigade and the mechanised 9th Field Brigade RA, took part in a major exercise on Salisbury Plain in September of that year. It was intended to demonstrate the effectiveness of integrated mechanised formations and to learn from it so that the organisations and tactics for future armoured formations could be evolved. Unfortunately, other factors which were no doubt considered pertinent at the time led the exercise controllers to place unrealistic constraints on the armoured formations with the result that the War Office adjudged the formation and modernisation of mobile armoured forces to have a lower priority than the renovation of infantry divisions.

Other nations had been watching developments very closely, none more so than the Germans, who quickly realised the potential of such a force. Although the Germans did not form their first tank battalion until 1934, by the end of 1935 they had three tank brigades and by 1939 they had six armoured divisions, whilst the British Army had but two incomplete divisions. An examination of some of the tactics employed by Guderian in 1940 and Patton in 1944 show a marked resemblance to the manner in which Hobart had deployed his forces in those 1934 exercises.

By 1936 it was apparent to even the most optimistic that Hitler's rearmament programme was a serious and deadly threat. Tank development in Britain was in the doldrums, hindered by lack of money to explore new avenues and by rigid thinking which would not accept that mechanised warfare would be anything more than an extension of the tactics in being in 1918.

The picture was very black indeed. The A6 or Vickers 16 tonner which had been offered to the British Army in 1928 had been dropped as too expensive, but it was a very fine tank indeed for its time, and if it had seen service and been allowed the normal process of evolution doubtless we would have been in a far better position in 1939.

Fig. 1.7 Vickers medium Mark III, A6 E3

Categories of Tanks Between the Wars

Because there had not been any major conflict involving two equally balanced
armoured formations since 1918, various distinct categories of tanks had come into
being untried and untested in battle. The categories that could be identified in
the world's armies were firstly the very light tank designed to accompany the infantry
in the role of a heavy infantry weapon carrier. This type of vehicle was particularly
favoured by the French, and the Renault FT tanks are a typical example. Running
in parallel with this concept was the fast light tank developed mainly by the British
as a reconnaissance vehicle. The significant mobility advantage they presented
in relation to other armoured fighting vehicles (AFVs) was gradually eroded as more
protection and heavier armament was added with the idea of increasing their effectiveness.

The other two categories were the medium tank, which was a fast, thinly protected
but reasonably well-armed tank designed as an exploitation vehicle. To complement
this concept the heavily protected infantry tank that would be immune to enemy
fire was conceived. It was accepted that because of the weight of armour the tank
would be slow, but as it was only needed to accompany the infantry at walking pace
this was not seen to be a disadvantage.

Because everything was subordinated to protection, its firepower suffered to the
extent that it was virtually impotent against anything except the lightest opposition.
The ultimate British tank of this type was the 40-ton Churchill of 1941 with 4-inch
armour protection but only mounting a 40 mm gun (see Fig. 1.9).

Fig. 1.8 Cruiser Mark III

Fig. 1.9 A22 tank infantry Mark IV "Churchill" (Mark I), 38.7 tons

LESSONS FROM THE SECOND WORLD WAR

Tank Characteristics

By the middle of the second World War it was apparent that neither the light tanks nor the infantry tanks had any place on the battlefield. Additionally, the medium tank exploitation role was being called into question, as it was found that these tanks still had to fight and win the battle before they could be used for exploitation and their armament was simply not up to the task. With the ever-present problem of limited resources, it was neither possible nor reasonable to be able to expect to hold these forces in reserve until a suitable situation presented itself.

We now see how the tactics of the armoured formations were influencing the design of the fighting vehicles. Each country was searching for a design which provided a balance between firepower, mobility and protection. Of course these are not the only characteristics of armoured fighting vehicles, but they are probably the three most important. Other aspects which have to be considered to a greater or lesser extent are:

Communications.	Reliability.
Surveillance.	Maintainability
Silence.	Endurance.
Cost.	

Priorities of Characteristics

The role of any combat vehicle is to carry a payload whether it be combat supplies or a gun turret. The priority given to any particular characteristics and the space and proportion of weight devoted to any particular characteristic will depend on the role envisaged for that vehicle. For a reconnaissance vehicle high priority will be given to mobility. As regards main battle tanks (MBTs), since the Second World War all nations have tended to give firepower a high priority, with equal priority being shared between protection and mobility.

Throughout the greater part of the Second World War the tank was always vulnerable to an enemy anti-tank defence system based on a large high-velocity gun which was often a towed gun, although sometimes it was mounted on some sort of self-propelled chassis. The sheer size of these guns made it technically impossible to mount them in conventional tanks of the early war days with their relatively small diameter turret rings. The Germans managed it at a later stage when they mounted the 88 mm on their Tiger tanks, but that tank had other problems which prevented it ever becoming a real success story.

One of the better designs to come out of the war was the British Centurion. Design work commenced in 1943 and a few prototypes were sent over to the continent in 1945 but never saw action. This design was the culmination of all the lessons learnt in the war, and it successfully provided a tank with a high-velocity (HV) gun that was the match of any tank on the battlefield, and yet the design was sufficiently well balanced to provide good protection and a reasonable level of mobility.

The first Centurions mounted the 76.2-mm gun and the 20-mm Polson cannon, but by 1948 the Mark III was mounting a 84-mm high-velocity (HV) gun and was a very efficient fighting machine incorporating a stabilising system for the gun. The basic concept for this tank, although fitted with the larger 105-mm gun at a later date,

Fig. 1.10 PZ KW VI "Tiger"

Fig. 1.11 Centurion Mark I 76.2-mm and 20-mm cannon

remained unchanged through its long and distinguished career. Indeed, it is still in service in many parts of the world today, and has been continually developed through 13 marks. In many ways the later Centurion could be used as a yardstick against which to measure the performance of any tank right up to and including the production of the M60 by the United States in 1960.

POSTWAR DEVELOPMENT

The Concept of the Main Battle Tank

Thus, it was convincingly demonstrated that the concept of a universal main battle tank (MBT) was viable. The line of development was set for the next 40 years with all the countries pursuing the same basic concept of a balanced design, tempered by national conceptions of operations on the battlefield giving differing weightings to the order of priority.

It is interesting to note that in 1956 the Germans, the French and the Italians started collaboration in their tank development and the FINABEL agreement aimed at producing a standard main battle tank. They had all expressed a desire to keep as close to 30 tons as possible, but difficulties arose over the interpretation of these requirements as each country gave different priorities and weightings to different characteristics. Eventually, as it became apparent that it would not be possible to produce a common vehicle, each country went its own way, with Germany and France producing the Leopard and the AMX 30. They are very different tanks. The Leopard mounts the UK 105-mm gun, has some measure of protection and weighs in at 40 tons, whilst the AMX 30 only weighs 34 tons but has very limited protection and mounts only a medium-velocity (MV) gun which cannot fire high-velocity (HV) kinetic energy (KE) rounds and is limited to chemical (CE) rounds. Yet both tanks stemmed from the same initial requirement.

A brief glance at various main battle tanks recently in production and of those currently coming off the production line show how national doctrine influences the priority afforded to these characteristics.

Israeli Priorities

The Israeli Army fervently believe in shock action and that armoured formations are the best way of achieving this. This presupposes a high degree of mobility in their armoured vehicles, but they also recognised that they would probably have to survive an initial onslaught, win the breakthrough battle and then still have enough troops left to initiate the necessary shock action to exploit their success. This led them into giving every attention to survivability, which gave rise to the production of the 56-ton Merkava tank which allocates high priority to protection, far higher than we have seen anyone else, except the British, afford to this characteristic since the Second World War.

Russian Priorities

At the other end of the scale we can see how the Soviet Union's armoured warfare philosophy has affected their production designs. After their experience of the German Blitzkrieg the Russians were determined to learn from it and develop their own tactics accordingly. They believe in the supremacy of the offensive, in the use of maximum force attacking on a wide front and of passing another complete formation through a spent one. They also place a great emphasis on speed and depth of penetration, bypassing opposition if necessary but setting formidable rates of advance. Of course they have massive resources to call upon, and whilst they are still prepared to devote the currently high proportion of their gross national product (GNP) to arms production they will be in a position to be able to apply the doctrine of attack *en masse*. With a conscript army drawn from a vast populace they can also be selective in their choice of tank crews and have the luxury of being able to select crews of smaller stature, which can hence lead to smaller tanks, whilst the Western Allies are restricted by the necessity to build tanks to meet the size of the 95 percentile man. The dimensions of the "95 percentile man" are those that will encompass 95% of the male population.

The principle of primacy of the offensive has two other important consequences. Accepting that their tanks will only be used occasionally as defensive weapons, it becomes sensible to accept a limited gun depression, currently about 5°. Figure 3.2 shows why most NATO nations specify a minimum of 10° if the tank is to be used effectively in a defensive role. This limitation of the gun depression bestows certain advantages to the tank designer and can help to keep down the height of the tank (and hence reduce the size of the target offered) as will be explained in Chapter 3.

The second effect is that the Russians give a different interpretation to the requirement for survivability. Because they visualise their tanks being employed in the offensive role, they will accept that ammunition can be stowed above the turret ring and that external long-range fuel tanks can be situated on the external rear decks and side track guards. These features allow the designer considerably more flexibility than his Western counterpart, who is constrained by many more safety aspects.

NATO Countries Priorities

When the current British position on tank design philosophy and production is considered it is apparent that the size of the economic and engineering power base is also an influential factor. As tanks become more complex and expensive in real terms the orders required to sustain a production run are increasingly hard to find. Thus it is not possible to contemplate a half fleet replacement, and any design accepted must be capable of remaining in service for at least 15 years.

While predominance is given to firepower in the Chieftain tank, it is also apparent that a fair proportion of the priority weighting is given to protection. This is due not only to the evaluation of the immediate threat but also to a requirement to go some way to meeting future likely threats. The apparent low priority given to mobility should be taken in context with the mobility offered by Leopard 1 and AMX 30 at the expense of protection. The Chieftain represents a continuous increase in British mobility levels since 1945 and met the levels required by the Army when it came into service in 1964. As explained in Chapter 4, the power plant for an armoured fighting vehicle (AFV) is a very special animal and development of an 600-800 bhp tank engine is an expensive and time-consuming business. Elsewhere, on the Continent and in the United States, there is a commercial market for engines of similar size and the problems of producing special AFV engines are greatly eased.

As we have already seen, both the Germans and the French have been down the road of good firepower and mobility at the expense of protection. With Leopard 2 we see the Germans shifting back towards greater levels of protection, recognising that the likely scenario for any future battle in Europe will require them to halt the enemy advance before they engage in full-scale mobile warfare and utilise the effect of shock action to the full.

An examination of US doctrine discloses some different factors. The first is that as a superpower isolated from the European land mass and with worldwide defence commitments the importance of the tank as a weapon of war and an accoutrement

to the exercise of power is overshadowed by the requirement for naval and air power.
The exclusion and acceptance of technology has been nowhere greater than in the
United States. This has often led them to believe that a quantum jump in any particular field is just round the corner. It has also led them down several unfamiliar
paths with disappointing results. After the successful M60 series the Americans
flirted with advanced technology with the MBT 70, but it proved to be too expensive, complex and with a weapon system unsuited to its task. This led to a reap-
praisal of the 53 tonnes tank and with a realistic price ceiling. The vast resources
available in the States and the potential size of the final contract allowed the Americans the luxury of placing two validation contracts with Chrysler and General
Motors. Both the versions offered had many points of similarity, but in 1976 it was
announced that the contract had been awarded to Chrysler to produce their XM 1
(General Abrams) tank. Now in service, this tank is conventional in its four-man
crew layout, but features composite Chobham-type armour and a gas turbine engine.
It currently mounts a 105-mm rifled gun, but the design is such that a 120-mm gun,
either rifled or smooth bore, could be fitted without too much difficulty.

SIMILARITIES AND DIFFERENCES

This brief survey has traced the development of the tank from early beginnings
to the present day. We can also detect a remarkable similarity in many features
of current design. Decades of experience have confirmed aspects of successful
design evolution and has shown where unconventional forays into the unknown have
met with disaster. The lessons of experience are well known by all nations and
have distilled over the years into a set of design principles that find a remarkable
level of agreement. It is in the final design that national defence priorities and
military interpretations of that requirement influence the shape of the tank that
comes off the production line.

Fig. 1.12 General Abrams tank

SELF TEST QUESTIONS

QUESTION 1   What were the circumstances that led to the introduction of the
              tank in the First World War?

              Answer   ....

                        ....

                        ....

QUESTION 2   What was the main advantage and disadvantage of the rhomboid
              shape and the complete overall track?

              Answer   ....

                        ....

                        ....

                        ....

QUESTION 3   What was the main innovation of the Christie tank of the 1920s?

              Answer   ....

                        ....

QUESTION 4   What were the four categories of tanks that could be identified
              between the wars?

              Answer a.   ....

                     b.   ....

                     c.   ....

                     d.   ....

QUESTION 5   What were the two categories of tanks that the British used for
              most of the Second World War?

              Answer a.   ....

                     b.   ....

QUESTION 6   By the middle of the Second World War each nation was searching
              for a design which would provide a balance. What were the three
              characteristics that had to be balanced?

              Answer a.   ....

                     b.   ....

                     c.   ....

QUESTION 7   Name four other aspects which might need consideration to achieve
a design balance.

Answer   ....

....

....

....

QUESTION 8   What effect does the Russian principle of primacy of the offensive
have upon their tank design philosophy?

Answer   ....

....

....

QUESTION 9   What considerations motivated the Israelis to design the Merkava
tank?

Answer   ....

....

QUESTION 10   What innovations are incorporated in the American General Abrams
tank?

Answer   ....

....

Answers on page 219.

2. Tank Fire Power

INTRODUCTION

Once the initial idea of using a mechanical device to cross ditches and barbed wire entanglements had proved feasible, the potential of such a machine as a weapon platform quickly became apparent. By the end of the First World War the favourite calibre was 57 mm, with few tanks mounting anything larger. These guns would be classed as low-to-medium velocity by today's standards and their battlefield effectiveness was strictly limited. As tanks began to don thicker armour for their own protection, the need for higher velocity guns led to longer barrelled versions.

The increase in muzzle velocity obtained tended to satisfy the requirement at the time and calibres remained relatively small. Thus the Crusader cruiser tank of 1941 only mounted a 40-mm gun, but this was a high-velocity armour-defeating weapon. It was not until the superiority of the German tank guns became so marked as to dominate battlefield tactics that the Allies began seriously to consider mounting heavier and more powerful weapons.

ROLES

The tank can carry a very versatile system of weapons. Its most important role is taken to be "Shock Action", but as a corollary this must be the disablement and destruction of enemy armoured vehicles of a similar weight class, preferably at ranges greater than the effective range of the enemy's armament. Other roles will be the destruction of lightly or unarmoured vehicles, men in the open and hard pinpoint targets such as emplacements and fortified areas.

As part of subsidiary miscellaneous roles we should now add the requirement to fire a carrier shell containing smoke or illuminant. The capability to engage helicopters is also a highly desirable characteristic.

NIGHT FIGHTING

Ideally, a tank should be able to fight equally effectively by day and night, but the problems of firing accurately at night at long range are not easily overcome.

Searchlight illumination can be effective up to 1000 m, but disclosure of the tank's position when the light is switched on is a serious disadvantage. A drill whereby a flanking tank briefly illuminates the target for another tank can be successful with well-trained crews in a defensive position where the ranges to likely targets are known, but there still remains the problem of target acquisition.

Active infrared (IR) systems initially allowed the user some protection against visual detection, but with the proliferation of IR systems on the battlefield this protection has virtually disappeared. Various alternatives are discussed under sighting systems.

SELECTION OF THE MAIN ARMAMENT

When we think of tanks we normally think of a tracked vehicle with a rotating turret mounting a gun. This may not always be the case and the choice lies between a versatile system capable of engaging a variety of targets or a specialised system in which the vehicle has only one role. In the latter case we can very easily produce a very light vehicle that is capable of destroying much heavier vehicles but is not capable of undertaking any other task. An anti-tank guided weapons carrier such as Striker is a good example.

If, on the other hand, it is decided that a more versatile vehicle is required not only to destroy enemy tanks but also to carry out a wide variety of other tasks, then the current choice is a high-velocity gun. The weights and leading dimensions of some typical fire weapons are shown in Fig. 2.1. It is noticeable that there is a considerable size and weight penalty to pay if you wish to increase from a medium-velocity gun to a high-velocity gun of the same calibre.

TARGET CHARACTERISTICS

Before the main armament can be selected it is necessary to decide what the target will be. The most likely targets we will need to engage are enemy tanks which threaten our position. The size of target presented to an observer depends not only on its physical dimensions but also on the way it is being used tactically. Tanks in the open present a comparatively large target, but it is likely that they will be moving and this reduces the chance of hitting them. In other circumstances tanks present very much smaller targets. If, for example, the enemy is merely observing, then he will probably be in a turret down position. But if he intends to fire he will move into a hull down position (see Fig. 2.2). In this position the hull and running gear are concealed but the turret above the trunnions is exposed. Gun depression is important here. If the enemy's gun has a limited depression of, say, less than 180 mils (10°) and the tank is sited on a reverse slope, it will frequently need to expose rather more of itself to take up a firing position.

In any event the size of a target can be expressed as the angle it presents at the gun, and this angle is called target subtense. It is a useful way of describing the size of a target because it takes into account not only the target's physical dimensions but also the range at which it is being engaged. Rather obviously, the further away the target is, the smaller the error you can afford if you want to hit it.

$$\text{Subtense (m)} = \frac{\text{height (or width) (m) x 1000}}{\text{range (m)}}$$

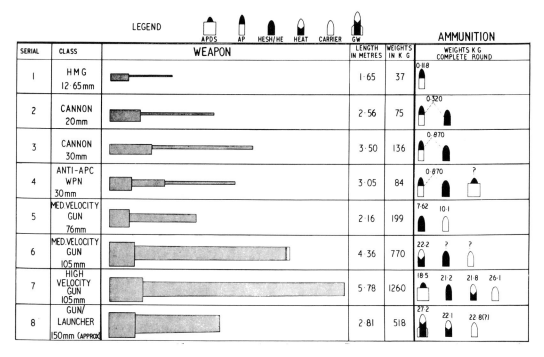

Fig. 2.1 Weights and leading dimensions of typical weapons

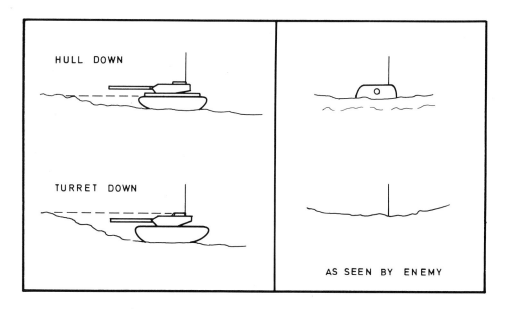

Fig. 2.2 Hull and turret down positions

Target width is normally greater than its height and it is in the vertical plane that weapon system errors are greater, so normally the target subtense refers to height. The dimensions of a tank turret will vary but generally they are in the order of 1 m high and 1.5-2 m wide. Thus the hull down tank at a 1000 m has a vertical subtense of about 1 mil.

The range of 1000 m is convenient for calculation of target subtenses, but the actual range at which targets will appear will depend on a variety of factors of which inter-visibility has the single greatest influence. In desert conditions targets may well appear at 6000 m or more and engagement ranges of 3000 m may be common. How-ever, in North West Europe the contours of the ground, the forests, buildings and other obstacles to vision are so distributed that 75% of all targets appear at ranges of 2000 m or less, and very few targets indeed are seen over 4000 m.

It is always difficult to be specific about the ranges that should be considered "short" or "long", but as a rough guide 0-1000 m is short range, 1000-2000 m is medium range and 2000-4000 m is long range.

Apart from the small size of the target, the next greatest problem is the short time the target is exposed. If the enemy tank or armoured vehicle is being commanded correctly, then it will only offer a fleeting target as it moves from one piece of cover to another. This will probably be the only time a whole vehicle is offered as a target. On other occasions it is likely that only the turret will be exposed. Exposure times will vary greatly with the nature of the cover available on the battlefield, the dif-ficulty of ground the AFV has to negotiate and the agility of the vehicle. As a general yardstick, maximum exposure times at maximum range might be 1-1½ minutes, but as the range decreases so will exposure time and at battle ranges it will rarely be more than 20-25 seconds.

From this it can be seen that for any armour-defeating weapon the main characteris-tics must be:

1.   High lethality. The target must be defeated whatever form of attack is chosen.

2.   Extreme accuracy. The target likely to be presented is very small, even at relatively short ranges.

3.   High speed of engagement. The target will only present itself for short periods and it must be acquired and engaged during that exposure time.

DAMAGE CRITERA

Choice of Weapon

The choice of weapon has already been discussed in general terms, and if the cur-rent choice of armies equipped with modern MBTs is considered it is found that there is a disparity both in choice of calibre and choice of barrel type.

The Russians and the Germans have both chosen smooth bore guns of 125 mm and 120 mm respectively for their T72 and Leopard 2 tanks, whereas the British retain a 120-mm rifled barrel for the Challenger. The Americans are initially fitting a 105-mm rifled gun in the M1 Abrams, although they have announced their intention to fit a 120-mm smooth bore gun at a later stage.

"M" Kill

To understand the wide variety of choice it is first necessary to examine the target and the various methods of defeating it. There are several ways of rendering a tank ineffective on the battlefield. If a tank is incapable of exercising controlled movement on the battlefield, then it is classified as an "M" kill. This could be due to crew injury or to damage to the tracks, suspension and final drive or to anywhere in the power train which would render it immobile. If the tank became immobile in a position on the battlefield where it can still engage the enemy, then it may be able to influence the battle for a while, but if it can see to fire it can also be seen to be fired at, so without the ability to manoeuvre into a new position it is unlikely to survive very long. In any mobile battle the casualty will either be overtaken by the enemy or the battle will have moved forward, allowing it to be recovered.

"F" Kill

The second partial damage criterion is the fighting or firepower "F" kill. This definition covers the occasion when the main armament cannot be operated either because it is damaged beyond repair or because the crew are no longer capable of operating it.

"K" Kill

The term "knocked out" is often loosely used to describe a tank which is no longer functional on the battlefield, but any tank which is immobilised, incapable of firing and damaged beyond repair is properly described as a "K" kill.

"P" kill

These previous definitions can be fairly widely applied or adapted to all types of armoured fighting vehicles, although there is the additional criterion of a "P" Kill which applies to MICVs when at least 40% of the passengers are disabled or incapable of performing their battle function.

Penetration and Lethality

Although the types of kill are easily understood and defined, it is not always so easy to achieve a desired degree of lethality. Penetration itself may not be enough to produce any one of the types of kill. There are several well-documented instances in the Yom Kippur war of tanks being hit and penetrated several times by hand-held infantry anti-tank weapons and the crews being unaware of the damage until much later. This introduces the vexed question of lethality which is usually described as the percentage chance of a particular projectile producing an M, F or K kill against the target. It is a vexed question because if a kinetic energy projectile penetrates with sufficient residual energy it will normally produce a kill, whereas the direction of attack and the point of impact is extremely relevant to the lethality of an attack by a hollow charge projectile.

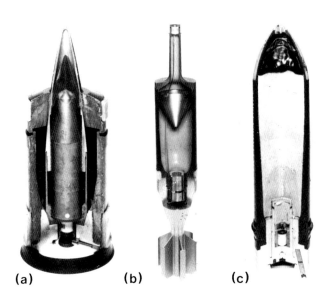

Fig. 2.3 Kinetic energy, hollow charge and HESH projectiles

WARHEAD EFFECTS

Kinetic Energy Attack

In order to prevent an armoured fighting vehicle taking any further part in the battle the vehicle must be incapacitated in one of the ways described. Whatever type of incapacitation is effected, it can only be achieved by extending a considerable amount of energy. This "energy package" can be delivered to the target, apart from nuclear weapon effects, in one of two ways. A projectile can be given a certain amount of energy by the attacking vehicle and sent towards the target: if the projectile has sufficient residual energy when it arrives at the target to overmatch the capability and strength of the target material to resist penetration, then it will penetrate and should obtain a kill. This is described as a kinetic energy (KE) attack where the penetration is achieved by means of the residual energy of the projectile.

Kinetic energy shot behaves in accordance with the law of physics.

$$K.E. = \tfrac{1}{2} MV^2$$

Increasing the mass (M) of the shot increases its energy, but the real payoff comes from increasing its velocity (V). If the diameter of the shot fills the whole gun barrel, then it can easily be made very heavy, but it then becomes difficult to accelerate to the required velocity within the length of the barrel. Additionally, a large diameter solid shot will expend more energy penetrating a given thickness or armour compared to a projectile which has the same mass but a smaller diameter. Consequently, the larger shot is not only less effective at the target but it is difficult to give it the necessary velocity.

Early attempts to overcome this problem included the use of the "squeeze bore" principle whereby the outer casing of the shot was literally squeezed to a smaller diameter at the end of the barrel. Although quite effective in the smaller calibre anti-tank guns of the early days of the Second World War, it has distinct limitations and can now only be considered a historical curiosity.

Another method employed for a time featured a core of dense material surrounded by a lighter case. When the projectile arrived at the target the outer, lighter material was stripped off, leaving the inner core to penetrate. Although more efficient than the full calibre shot, this type still suffers from ballistic inefficiency, air resistance on the relatively large frontal area causing a large drop in velocity which seriously degrades the penetrative power of the shot at anything more than very short ranges.

Towards the end of the Second World War the first really effective solution to the problem was developed in the form of the armour piercing discarding sabot (APDS) shot. A very dense penetrator is surrounded by a light "pot" which presents a large base area in the barrel and allows the relatively light projective (compared to a full calibre solid shot projectile) to be accelerated very quickly up the barrel. Once outside the barrel the "pot" falls off, allowing the smaller diameter shot to travel on towards the target. The shot normally has a ballistic outer shell to make it more efficient in flight. This ballistic casing shatters on arrival at the target, leaving the solid inner cone to penetrate. Although simple in conception, it is difficult to manufacture rounds that give a consistent performance, and as protection levels increase the mass and size of the solid cone must also increase, so we come back to the same problem of velocity versus mass.

Depth of penetration at the target will depend not only on the residual energy of the shot but also on its shape and size. The shape of the curve at the head of the penetrator is most important, as it must not only be able to pierce the armour but the shoulders of the shot must also support the remainder so that it does not break up on its way through the armour. If for a given mass the diameter of the shot is reduced and its length increased, then for the same residual velocity the shot will penetrate further, as it is working on a smaller cross-sectional area of the armour. The ratio of length-to-diameter is called the "slenderness" ratio, and although any projectile with a ratio in excess of 7:1 cannot be spin stabilised it is not until they reach a ratio of approximately 20:1 that they can be called "long rods". The long rod penetrator is now seen as the most significant advance for many years.

Hollow Charge Warhead

The second method attack is whereby a projectile carrying an energy package is delivered to the target. This can either be by a projectile fired from a gun, by a guided weapon or possibly by an aerially delivered projectile. The projectile contains a chemical energy(CE) or explosive package which could be one of three main types. By far the most important is the "hollow charge" or "shaped charge" device, often referred to as high explosive anti-tank (HEAT).

A simple explosion of the amount of high explosive that can normally be contained within the shell fired by a tank gun is unlikely to do lethal damage to an MBT: so means must be used to direct the energy of the explosion. The most effective and widely used method is to shape the charge so that the total energy available is directed into the target. This is achieved by manufacturing the charge in the shape of an inverted cone around a metal liner. When the charge is detonated the explosion is directed towards the target in the form of a narrow jet of extremely high energy which is a mixture of gas and fragments from the metal cone. The effectiveness of the jet depends upon the diameter of the cone, and hence the calibre of the gun, the nature of the metal liner and the "stand off" distance from the target at which the charge was detonated.

The effect of this type of attack is severely degraded if the charge is spun, so a hollow charge projectile must be fin stabilised and if it is to be fired from a rifled gun it must have some form of slipping driving bands to limit its spin rate to an acceptable level. Although the total depth of penetration achieved can be very impressive for a relatively small cone diameter, lethality is low unless it over-matches the target by at least 33%, that is to say the charge could have penetrated a target at least half as thick again. If it matches this criterion and has an exit hole diameter in excess of 1 inch, then the effect on the target is likely to be devastating.

Not only will the jet continue into the target vehicle with considerable residual energy but it will also bring in a certain amount of "spall" from the sides of the hole that it has made. The spall will spread out inside the vehicle and the high energy hot metal fragments travelling at considerable speed will have a highly destructive effect on ammunition, equipment and crew.

This form of attack is ideally suited to ATGW where the projectile is unspun and travelling at relatively low speeds. If the projectile strikes the target at very high velocities the fuze will not be able to initiate the charge at the correct stand-off distance and the effect will be degraded. Hence, if the projectile is to be fired from a gun, not only must its spin be limited but so must its velocity, thus reducing the chance of a hit. This used to be a considerable disadvantage, but modern developments, particularly advances in fuze design, have meant that HEAT projectiles can be fired at higher velocities, so ensuring accuracy whilst achieving correct stand off distances.

The need for slipping driving bands on HEAT projectiles fired from rifled guns sounds simple, but they are extremely difficult to design and manufacture with consistent results; and they reduce the cone diameter inside the warhead. Any-thing which reduces the cone diameter of the charge is in turn reducing the effectiveness of the projectile. Although a reduction in cone diameter is always detrimental, the effect is most marked in the smaller calibres (e.g. 75 mm) and less so in the larger calibres of 110 mm and greater.

High Explosive Squash Head

The second form of chemical energy attack is by high explosive squash head or HESH, the American term for which is HEP or high explosive plastic. In this form of attack the explosive is contained in a thin-walled projectile which collapses when the target is struck, allowing the plastic explosive to spread. A base fuze then detonates the explosive which sends shock waves through the armour. Reflection from the internal armour surface leads to an overmatch in the armour which then fails, causing a large scab and fragments to fly off inside the vehicle. The success of HESH against armour depends on the explosive forming a suitably "shaped pat" on the outside of the armour plate before it is detonated. This poses several problems, as it can be appreciated that if the projectile arrives at a very acute angle the explosive will not form a cohesive mass and consequently its effective-ness will be greatly reduced. Similarly, if the projectile arrives on the target with very high residual velocity the explosive can be dispersed before the fuze is initiated. The latter problem is easily resolved by regulating the muzzle velocity (MV), but its consequence is a lower hit chance because of the higher trajectory. HESH can be defeated relatively easily by providing a discontinuity in the path of the shock wave. Thus any form of spaced armour will defeat HESH, although the outer plate will almost certainly be destroyed.

The major advantage of HESH lies in its usefulness as a multipurpose round. It is approximately 90% as effective as a conventional HE round against soft targets and considerably better than HE against bunkers and buildings. It has a devastating effect against lightly armoured vehicles and even if a kill is not obtained against a heavily armoured vehicle it is likely to have considerable secondary effects, including damage to the optical equipment and antennae. In common with HEAT, it gives a realistic anti-tank capability to a medium-velocity gun but, unlike HEAT, it is a genuine dual purpose round.

Miznay Schardin Effect

The third form of chemical energy attack uses the Miznay Schardin effect: it is a method of arranging the charge to project a self-forming fragment at the target. It is not particularly well suited for use in projectiles and is mostly found in mines and similar devices.

Comparison of Kinetic Energy and Chemical Energy Attack

However good the target effects of chemical energy attack may be, it must always be delivered at a lower velocity than a kinetic energy shot and it must therefore always suffer from problems of relative inaccuracy and longer engagement times. Thus a kinetic energy round is generally regarded as the prime tank-killing round in the armoury of anti-tank guns, although there is a place for chemical energy as a secondary form of attack and some attempts have been made to design a lightweight MBT relying on a lower velocity CE round as the main armament.

CHOICE OF LAUNCHER

Like all advances, long rods are not without their own disadvantages. In this case one of the main problems lies in the external ballistics of the projectile, because spin stabilised projectiles must have a low slenderness ratio. This is obviously impossible with a long rod, so it must remain unspun and be fin stabilised. Once it is decided that all the rounds to be fired can be unspun and fin stabilised, then the next logical step is to ultilise a smooth bore gun. This has the advantage of being able to use higher energy propellants without the normal corollary of the greatly increased wear that is associated with rifled barrels, and it leads to greatly increased muzzle velocities and an inherent increase in the chance of a hit. By drastically reducing the significance of barrel wear it could become a significant battle-winning factor, as rifled barrels have a definite life span measured in effective full charges (EFCs). An artillery gun will fire many rounds before it is condemned, and its life span will be measured by its fatigue life, whereas a tank gun must be consistent and with the greatly increased charge rates employed its life span will be measured in hundreds of rounds rather than thousands.

If a rifled gun is chosen it is perfectly feasible to use slipping driving bands on all projectiles, but there must be some doubt on how effective these will be for MVs in excess of 2000 m/s. However, a rifled barrel does mean that it still is possible to fire a wide variety of ammunition, which allows the vehicle to fulfill its traditional role as a multi-purpose battle tank rather than solely as an anti-tank weapon.

Both armour piercing fin stabilised discarding sabot (APFSDS) and HEAT fin stabilised (FS) can be satisfactorily fired from both smooth bore and rifled guns, but
because of the weight of the explosive that needs to be carried in the projectile
it is currently only feasible to fire HESH from a rifled gun. To make a HESH round
fin stabilised would require such a long tail that it would be almost impossible to
fit it into the chamber of the gun, let alone pack the necessary propellant into the
available space.

Readers who wish to know more about the attack of armour are advised to read
Volume III of this series.

ACCURACY

Sources of Error

In ideal circumstances an enemy target should be defeated at a range at which he
is incapable of effective retaliation. This requires an accurate gun where the
errors have been reduced to a minimum. Even in a simple combination of gun,
ammunition and sighting system, the errors are fairly complex and comprise some
twenty-five components called the error budget. They can be classified as errors
of elevation or line and can be either permanent biases, variable biases or random
errors. They are normally analysed in five groups:

      1.   Production, maintenance and setting up errors.

      2.   Correction of the moment.

      3.   Range determination.

      4.   Gunners' errors.

      5.   Residual inherent errors.

Production, Maintenance and Setting Up Errors

Sound design is essential for accuracy. The gun must be designed with production
methods in mind so that it is capable of being made within the specified tolerances.
Once it is in service it must be capable of being maintained in the field and a gun
operated in arduous conditions must still remain within its design limits. The design
must also allow for accurate alignment of the gun and sight.

Correction of the Moment

Correction of the moment is a familiar artillery term which in tank gunnery refers
to the internal errors in the system. The first problem is to determine exactly what
happens to the barrel when the projectile is fired.

Because saving weight is all-important, tank gun barrels are designed to be as light
as possible, but because it is necessary to accelerate the projectile to a very high
velocity, the barrel also tends to be rather long. The long and relatively lightweight barrel is normally fired at very small angles of elevation, so it will inevitably
droop a little at the end. This will not be discernible to the naked eye, but it is

apparent that if you link the sight to the breech end of the gun it will not accurately reflect the position of the muzzle. It has proved less than satisfactory to make a standard correction for this error and the problem has been approached in two ways. First the bearing point of the gun has been moved as far forward as possible and second a device has been provided on the sighting system which allows the gunner constantly to check the position of the muzzle. This "Muzzle Reference System" is essentially a light source mounted on the turret which projects a beam onto a mirror fixed rigidly to the end of the barrel. The reflected image appears in the gunner's sight and it is a simple matter to adjust the sight to maintain the correct relationship between sight and gun at the muzzle.

Range Determination

In any sighting system there will be an error due to sight offset and the drift of the projectile downrange. The further the sight head is placed away from the axis of the barrel the greater the offset at anything other than the range at which the sight line is set to coincide with the axis of the barrel, normally 1000 m. British ammunition is given a right-hand spin and so tends to drift to the right. This can be plotted and, together with the sight offset, compensation can be made for it within the sighting system.

Gunners' Errors

There are many variable biases which are subject to human error and by utilising special equipment these can be largely avoided. The process of aligning gun and sight is known as "zeroing" or "shooting in". It consists of firing several shots at a target at a known range and then adjusting the sights to coincide with the fall of shot. This procedure has several inherent problems and although ideally it should be conducted at regular intervals it is neither practicable nor desirable to do so in peacetime or on the battlefield. An alternative is to use optical devices for initial sight alignment and the muzzle reference system to detect any subsequent misalignment.

Residual Inherent Errors

Mechanical errors in the sight linkage can be caused by poor design leading to play in the linkage but the greatest cause of error is temperature differentials affecting the link bars. Compensating systems can be adopted, such as on Chieftain where a liquid circulating through hollow link bars maintains a constant temperature.

It has already been shown that the barrel is a complex device, the behaviour of which is not yet fully understood. As the temperature of the barrel increases with firing it becomes increasingly sensitive to temperature differentials caused either by rain on the upper surfaces or, more likely, by wind blowing on its sides. These can be greatly reduced by covering the barrel with a thermal sleeve, and most modern tank guns employ this method. The effect of gun vibration at the moment of firing is not amenable to simple analysis or solution and can lead to considerable inconsistencies known as "jump".

Trunnion tilt occurs when the firing tank is on laterally sloping ground and one gun trunnion is higher than the other. In these circumstances, when the gun is elevated the relationship between the gun, the sight and the line of sight to the target is not the same as if the trunnions were level. If the angle of tilt is known the effect can be calculated; a simplified diagram showing the problem is shown in Fig. 2.4. The first figure shows a gun (A) and a telescopic sight (S) when the gun is level.

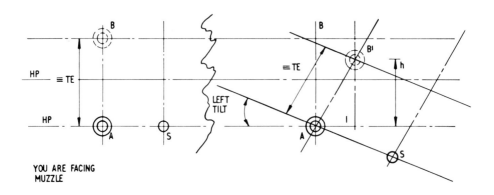

Fig. 2.4 Trunnion tilt

The gun is then elevated to take into account the range to the target (tangent elevation or TE), and although the line of sight to the target remains the same and hence the sight (S) remains in the same position the muzzle of the gun moves to position B.

But if the tank is on sloping ground and the gun trunnions are tilted as in the second figure, which is grossly exaggerated, the application of the same amount of TE moves the muzzle of the gun not to B but to B1. In this position the vertical component h is less than the required TE, so the gun will shoot low and because it has been displaced sideways a distance T it will shoot in the direction of the lower trunnion. The size of the error will depend not only on the amount of slope but also on the amount of TE which has to be applied. The bigger the TE, the greater the error. TE depends not only on range but also on muzzle velocity, so high-velocity ammunition is not as susceptible to trunnion tilt errors as low-velocity ammunition. Nevertheless, it can be a significant component of the error budget. If we have some method of measuring the actual tilt, then it is possible to calculate the effect and introduce a compensation for it. This is one function of a computer controlled sighting system.

Artillery fire is very sensitive to meteorological conditions, and great efforts are made to obtain sufficient information to make the necessary compensations. In tank gunnery, the ranges are much shorter, the velocity of armour-piercing projectiles is much higher and hence the time of flight is so greatly reduced that the effect of side, head or tail winds is generally very small. However, side winds of about 5 m/s or greater can make either types of ammunition miss the target at quite ordinary ranges. Side winds have the greatest effect, but head or tail winds can also cause significant errors in elevation. In computerised sighting systems a wind probe can measure the direction and strength of the wind at the position of the firing tank, but cannot predict the conditions along the flight path of the projectile. In circumstances where the latter is significantly different from the former some method must be provided for the commander to inject into the system his estimate of the down range wind strength and direction.

As the gun wears, the velocity of the projectile fired from it will decrease and hence it will fire lower. With high-velocity APFSDS and similar rounds the effect is relatively small, but with lower velocity rounds it can be quite significant. If the rate of wear for each type of ammunition is known, it is a simple matter to feed the information into a computerised sighting system which will then automatically compensate for it.

A far greater effect on muzzle velocity is caused by the temperature of the charge. Cold charges do not produce the same amount of energy as those which are warm and charge temperature variations can cause significant muzzle velocity variations. This is also information which a computerised sighting system could use and correct, but there is a problem of which temperature to measure. The temperature outside the tank will probably not be the same as it is inside the tank or even inside the charge bins and racks. If the actual charge temperature is measured by means of a probe this presents problems of disconnections before the charge is loaded and such a cumbersome system would obviously be unsatisfactory. Even if the charge temperature could be measured accurately before the charge is loaded it could then vary greatly before firing according to the temperature of the gun chamber and the length of the time the charge remains in the chamber before firing. In most computerised sighting systems provision is made only for a gross estimate of the charge temperature to be fed into the system. This is intended only to differentiate between the extremes of a hot summer day or harsh winter conditions. Corrections for finer graduations of charge temperatures are not practicable.

RANGE ESTIMATION

Scale of the Problem

In the early days of tank gunnery there was little point in providing sophisticated remedies for minor errors when the error from incorrect range estimation could swamp all others. It is generally accepted that visual range estimation gives an error of around 30%, and even after considerable training this will only be reduced to about 20%. In peacetime this inherent error was often disguised by familiarity with the tank firing ranges by the crews and the gunnery instructors using them.

Correction from Fall of Shot

A satisfactory method in smaller calibre weapons of correcting for range estimation error is to fire at the target and then to correct from the fall of shot. This allows for full correction of the moment and takes account of down range weather conditions. Although this system can work well, it depends upon accurate observation of the fall of shot and in larger calibre weapons the obscuration effect when firing generally prevents accurate observation.

Other problems arise because this system increases the number of rounds required for each engagement and dramatically lengthens the time before the first round hits the target.

Optical Methods

Several armies have installed optical range finders, and there were a few examples in the 1939-45 war. Most optical range finders are difficult to install in a tank because in order to obtain the required levels of accuracy with stereoscopic systems it is necessary to have a wide optical base. This normally means that the system has to use the full width of the turret and in order to obtain a clear field of view it has to be in the upper part of the turret. There are consequent design constraints on the turret layout, and such a system requires the commander to put the tank in a position which will permit full width turret vision, which in turn may impose tactical penalties. In any case all optical systems are still subject to significant errors which increase with the square of the range, so that at longer ranges where the need for assistance in range estimation is greatest it is least accurate.

It also takes time to use as it may be necessary to take more than one reading.

The most commonly used types of optical range finders are stadiametric (where known target dimensions are matched against graduated marks in the sight), coincidence (split field) and stereoscopic. The latter is inherently the most accurate, but less than 50% are capable of obtaining a satisfactory image and all types of optical range-finding require constant training and practice if a reasonable level of proficiency is to be maintained.

Sub Calibre Ranging

The British adopted an optical range finder in the Conqueror tank, but it was not judged to be a great success and in later marks of Centurion a ballistic sub-calibre ranging system was adopted. The essential element of any sub-calibre ranging system is that the projectile fired should follow approximately the same trajectory as the main armament projectile. Because it is ballistically matched to the parent weapon it can then give information on trunnion tilt and down range meteorological conditions. As it is essential to observe the fall of the shot of the sub-calibre round, 100% tracer ammunition is required and the round must give a clear indication of target strike.

The characteristics of the system also point to its limitations. It is relatively slow in use, although not unacceptably so, and there will be a range limitation as the sub-calibre round can only be matched ballistically over a limited range bracket. There will also be observation problems at longer ranges, as most tracer rounds will burn out at a maximum of 2000-2500 m. The system does not present as many problems tactically as might be expected, because the source of small calibre rounds being fired on the battlefield is not easily discernible.

Laser Range Finding

The greatest single improvement in tank gun accuracy over recent years has been the introduction of the laser in the ranging system. Most tank laser sight (TLS) systems are incorporated into the sighting system, giving the gunner and the commander an instant and silent method of determining range to within 10 m accuracy and out to at least the effective weapon range limit. The sight itself is a fairly complex and expensive piece of equipment which introduces an element of potential unreliability into the weapon system, but its disadvantages of complexity are greatly outweighed by the enormous advantages it confers in terms of accuracy. There can be problems of false range readings due to dust, smoke or other objects partially obscuring the line of sight, but these can be very largely overcome by the use of logic circuits in the sight and by injecting an aiming mark which allows the gunner to compare the actual target size against the target size predicted by the determination of range due to the laser (see Fig. 2.5).

The Error Budget

Only the major sources of error have been discussed, but there are a total of twenty-five individual errors. The simplest way of analysing and classifying these errors is to break them down into three groups amenable to statistical treatment. Together they form the error budget. All its biases and errors can now be considered under the three groups given in Fig. 2.6.

There are three ways to deal with these errors. First they can be reduced or eliminated at source. The majority of permanent biases are amenable to some kind of technical solution, but this can be a complex and very expensive process. As always,

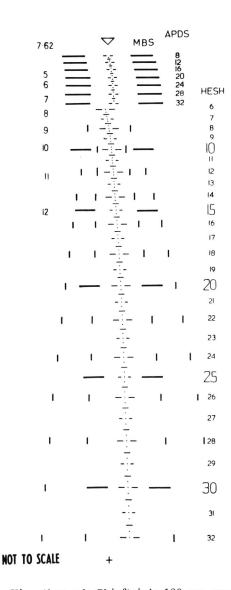

Fig. 2.5 View through Chieftain's 120-mm gun sight

the overall gain in accuracy must be weighed against cost. Second, they can be
measured, their effect computed and a correction applied. And third, they can be
accepted and, apart from obvious remedies, a technique of shooting can be evolved
that minimises their effects.

In the past, the third solution was the most common one, as equipment limitations
prevented any real progress being made in eliminating the majority of the sources
of errors. It was a sensible solution when it was still not possible to determine the
range to the target very accurately— by far the largest single source of error. With
the introduction of the laser as a range finding device this source of error was
eliminated. The other errors became significant and it then became sensible to look
for ways of correcting them, for example by using a computer based system.

Permanent biases	Variable biases	Random errors
Mean jump/Throw off	Muzzle boresight	Ballistic dispersion
Vertical/Lateral sight offset	Gun/alignment	Charge temperature (round to round)
Projectile drift	Shooting in	Propellant (lot to lot)
Barrel wear (mean)	Jump/Throw off	Laying error (round to round)
Range finding	Mechanical errors in sight system	Wind gusts
	Barrel wear (occasion to occasion)	
	Barrel bend	
	Definition of correct point of aim	
	Ballistic intervals in sight	
	Trunnion tilt	
	Bending of optical path	
	Changes of air density	
	Variations in charge temperatures	
	Wind effects	

Fig. 2.6 The Error Budget

Any computerised sighting system will endeavour to fulfil three main functions. It will continuously monitor the weapon system and the external ambient conditions that affect its performance and apply the necessary corrections. Then it will simplify the necessary gun and ballistic calculations and automatically adjust the sight. Finally it will greatly reduce the time taken to engage a target and greatly improve both the chance of hitting a moving target and of hitting a target from a moving tank.

A more detailed description of computerised sighting system is given in Volume IX of the series.

SECONDARY WEAPON SYSTEMS

Tanks have been armed with a variety of secondary weapons and the possibilities are virtually unlimited. The choice is driven by the battle role envisaged for the tank. If it is required to engage large numbers of infantry in the open and soft targets, such as buildings and bunkers, then a weapon mix that allows for a good HE capability will be provided. In some early Second World War tanks this was achieved by mounting a large calibre low-velocity gun with limited traverse: an example is the French Char B.

If it is considered that a large proportion of the secondary targets will be lightly armoured vehicles such as APCs or reconnaissance vehicles, then it is worth considering fitting a 20-30-mm cannon as can be seen on the French AMX 32. All these solutions have advantages, but they all suffer from the same problem of the large amount of space required for the weapon and its associated ammunition.

A medium machine gun of approximately 7.62-mm calibre offers the most effective and economical way of disabling men at short and medium ranges. This is normally mounted coaxially with the main gun because it allows the same sighting system to be used for both the main gun and the secondary weapon system. If the machine gun utilises the same mantlet as the main armament it also simplifies the problem of having to make yet another hole in the armour. It is normal for a further machine gun to be mounted on the commander's cupola. This gives him some independent firepower under his direct control to take on opportunity targets which either could not be engaged by the coaxial machine gun due to limitations of gun traverse or because the coaxial machine gun is already engaged with a previously selected target. As it is generally arranged on a pintle mount the commander's gun usually has sufficient elevation and flexibility for it to be used in an air defence role when required.

COMPUTER BASED FIRE CONTROL SYSTEM

The computer in a fire control system calculates and controls the gun lay for each engagement. It is fully programmable and can thus accommodate a full selection of ammunition natures as well as secondary armament. A simplified block diagram is shown in Fig. 2.7. Apart from calculating and controlling the gun lay, most systems provide the following facilities:

   Input/output monitoring

   Confidence checks of system adjustment and performance.

   First line fault diagnosis.

   Manual inputs for correcting:

       Successive shots from the observation of fire at long range.

       Faults in automatic inputs.

System outputs. The main outputs are:

Visual displays for both the commander and the gunner to assist them to set up the system, monitor its performance and warn them of faults.

Calculations of tangent elevation and aim-off for each engagement.

Automatic gun lay and tracking.

System inputs. The working information needed by the system is provided by the following three main methods:

Permanent. Magnetic tape or disc is used to load the computer with a working program and the standard ballistic data for each weapon/ammunition mix being used. It can only be changed by reloading program.

Semi-permanent. This is information that need only be changed occasionally:

   MPI adjusts. The difference between the point of aim and MPI for each weapon ammunition mix is determined by shooting-in and is entered manually.

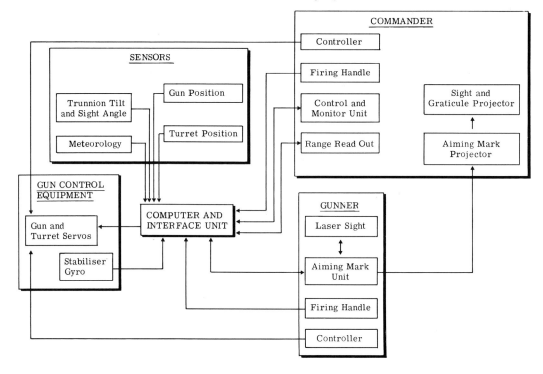

Fig. 2.7 A computer based fire control system

Barrel wear. The actual figure for main armament barrel wear is measured and entered manually. It is updated automatically whenever the gun is fired.

Charge temperature. A sensor input is feasible but of doubtful value. A manually entered standard figure is therefore used and only modified under extreme climatic conditions.

Engagement. Much of the necessary information depends on the particulars of the engagement. It is normally fed automatically to the computer as the engagement proceeds and cancelled when the engagement ends. Some of it can be entered manually if there is a system fault. The main items to be fed into the system are:

    The armament and the type of ammunition to be used.
    The target range and tracking rate.
    Trunnion tilt and angle of sight.
    Wind speed and direction.
    Air temperature and pressure.
    Relative gun position in azimuth and elevation.
    And finally corrections for line and elevation from the fall
        of shot must be entered manually.

Any computer based fire control system should be designed into the tank at the initial design stages or the advantages it can offer will be lost if the gun control system, such as the elevating mechanism, is not sufficiently accurate or responsive. It is essential that manufacturing tolerances are kept to a minimum and suitable modern gun control equipment is employed to permit accurate powered laying even at high tracking rates.

These systems are complex and expensive, but they make shooting remarkably quick and easy. They improve the chance of a hit at short ranges and dramatically increase the chance of a hit at a moving target.

FUTURE

Despite the adoption of 120-mm smooth bore guns by both the Germans and the French, the rifled 105-mm gun is still by far the most widely used calibre in Western tanks and is likely to remain so for some considerable time yet. There are well over 10,000 105-mm guns in service worldwide and most of them owe their origins to the British L7 rifled gun design, although many are now made under licence and are found in various marks of the American M60, the German Leopard 1, the Israeli Merkava and in a modified form in the Swedish "S" tank, the Swiss PZ 68 and, of course, in the later marks of the British Centurion MBT.

A wide variety of ammunition is available for this gun, including APFSDS with a slipping driving band (see Fig. 2.8). The Americans believe that it still has considerable potential and are incorporating it in the M1 Abrams tank. The British have announced their intention to continue with the 120-mm rifled barrel concept and the Russians successful 125-mm smooth bore gun adopted for later marks of the T64 and the T72 is likely to appear on their next tank.

Over the next decade there will probably be a steady improvement in the accuracy and penetrative powers of APFSDS with the utilisation of special materials to give greater mass and strength to the core. There will also be continued effort to improve the disruptive effect of the HEAT round without detracting from its penetrative ability in order to make it a general purpose round.

Probably the greatest developments will come in the fire control area where the possibilities seem unlimited. Technology is advancing so fast in this field that it becomes increasingly a management decision on how much it is sensible to invest in such equipment. Optronics and fire control equipment are accounting for an ever-increasing proportion of the total capital cost of modern battle tanks and as higher muzzle velocities increase the chance of a hit nearer to the theoretical maximum the cost of such sophisticated equipment must inevitably come under careful scrutiny.

However, the dramatic increase in the chance of hitting a moving target when a computerised sighting system is employed means that few modern tanks can afford to be without it if they wish to survive on the battlefield. This will lead to increases in the number of "director" type fire control systems that are available and that are linked to 24-hour thermal imaging sigting systems. The increased susceptibility of optronics in the hostile battlefield environment must inevitably lead to protective measures which could in turn mean simpler, fewer and less exposed devices or possibly additional armour and heavier vehicles.

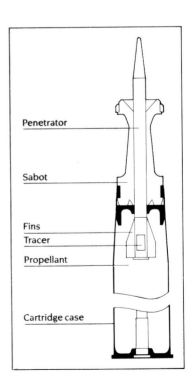

Penetrator

Sabot

Fins

Tracer

Propellant

Cartridge case

Fig. 2.8 APFSDS

SELF TEST QUESTIONS

QUESTION 1   What is the most important role of the tank and what are the other
              subsidiary roles?

              Answer   ....

                        ....

                        ....

                        ....

QUESTION 2   What are the normally accepted distances for short, medium and
              long range?

              Answer   ....

                        ....

                        ....

QUESTION 3   What are the four ways of defining a "kill"?

              Answer   a. ....

                        b. ....

                        c. ....

                        d. ....

QUESTON 4   What are the three main types of warhead effect?

              Answer   a. ....

                        b. ....

                        c. ....

QUESTION 5   What is the main advantage of HESH?

              Answer   ....

                        ....

QUESTION 6   Name the five groups which are normally used to analyse sources
              of error.

              Answer   a. ....

                        b. ....

                        c. ....

                        d. ....

                        e. ....

QUESTION 7   What are the possible methods of range estimation?

Answer   ....

....

....

....

QUESTION 8   What is meant by trunnion tilt?

Answer   ....

....

....

....

QUESTION 9   Why is a secondary weapon system desirable?

Answer   ....

....

....

QUESTION 10   What facilities would you expect to be provided by a computer
based fire control system?

Answer   ....

....

....

....

Answers on page 220.

3. Critical Dimensions

CRITICAL DIMENSIONS

A successful tank design should reflect a harmonious combination of the various characteristics of an armoured fighting vehicle. There are several constraints placed on the designer by the laws of physics and by other superimposed constraints. Tanks are inevitably heavy and complex machines and a modern battle tank would expect to be completely overhauled approximately every 4800 km. When the capital costs are added, it can be quickly realised that the true cost per mile or kilometer is very high indeed. It follows that it is essential that as high a proportion of non-tactical movement should be undertaken either on road tank transporters or by rail. In peacetime this helps to keep down costs, reduces maintenance loads and unnecessary damage to roads. It also enables tanks to be moved long distances relatively easily and in wartime it has the added advantage of allowing the tank to arrive on the battlefield in a mechanically sound condition and with relatively fresh crews. It follows that the overall size of the tank will be governed to some extent by this need to move it by rail or road.

Most countries impose statutory limits on the width of vehicles allowed on public highways and on the Continent and in the UK this is 2.5 m. Although these restrictions can be overcome by authorised exemptions, it is obvious that transportation by rail poses different problems where width restrictions are directly related to the physical constraints of the route restrictions. There is a multitude of various rail gauges applying to various routes and loads throughout the Continent, but the loading gauge which is generally accepted as the limiting factor is the TZ gauge (see Fig. 3.1). This allows access to most routes on the Continent, albeit with some traffic restrictions. It is interesting to note that the much more restricted UK rail loading gauge with a maximum of width of 2.74 m meant that Comet was the last British tank that could be transported by rail.

If we accept a need for rail transportation on the Continent we will have fixed the height and shape of the vehicle to fit into the gauge envelope and the width to a maximum of 3.54 m. This applies to the equipment that is permanently fixed and not to items such as the Commander's machine gun on the top of the cupola or the tank searchlight, as both items are relatively easily removed.

This width now becomes a finite limit which cannot be exceeded, and as we shall see it does impose considerable constraints upon the designer. On the other hand, rail gauge height limit is not such a constraint, as there are other factors which

41

Continental Gauge - "TZ"

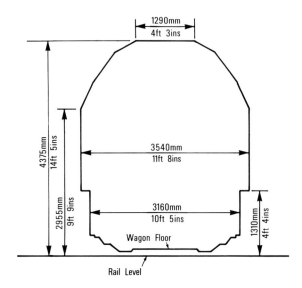

Fig. 3.1 Continental "TZ" rail gauge

prevail upon the designer to keep the height down. The foremost requirement is for the tank to offer the lowest possible silhouette to the enemy to avoid detection and present the smallest target. A glance at the vehicle data table (Table 1) reveals marked different national trends with Russian tanks being consistently the lowest and American tanks consistently the highest.

CHOICE OF WEAPON SYSTEM

The previous chapter dealt with tank firepower, and in this chapter we will see how the choice of weapon is the major influence on the final dimensions of the tank. The logical starting point is at the target. First we must decide what is the target? If we are sure that our tank is only ever going to be used against soft targets and infantry in the open, then we would be looking for a gun with a good HE performance and probably without a high-velocity capability. This will allow us to select a gun which for a given calibre will be comparatively light, small and with relatively little recoil energy to absorb. As a further bonus it is likely that the ammunition will also be relatively small, as the propellant charges weights will be smaller.

On the other hand, if we decide that the target is a tank or similar "hard" target, then we will be driven towards choosing a high-velocity gun with all the attendant problems of weight and size that are inextricably linked with fitting a modern large calibre tank gun. This in its turn brings problems to fitting the large buffers and recuperators necessary to absorb the gun recoil energy and allow the gun sufficient room to recoil at all angles of elevation and depression. It will also now be necessary to provide stowage space for much larger ammunition.

Once the size of the gun has been selected and the dimensions and other data made available to the designer, he can then approach the problem of fitting it into the turret. A prime consideration is the position of the trunnions on the gun and cradle and hence the inboard length of the gun that has to be accommodated inside the turret. The trunnions are normally near the point of balance of the gun as this keeps the load on the elevation gear to a minimum. This is important not only to reduce the strain and wear on the elevating gear but it is also very necessary if it is intended to fit automatic gun control equipment.

Another factor to consider is the need to load the gun and allow it to recoil at all angles of elevation and depression. The amount of depression given to a tank is a prime feature. A glance at Fig. 3.2 shows that the tank with limited depression of only 89 mils (5°) has to come further up the slope and expose more of itself to the enemy compared to the tank with 10° in order to engage the same target. Most Western nations consider this to be an essential feature, but this view is not shared by the Warsaw Pact countries who accept 89 mils depression.

If we accept the need for 180 mils depression then we must provide this over the full 1080 mils frontal arc and we must ensure that the gun clears all obstructions such as track guards or the driver's periscope within this arc. Obviously it would be relatively easy to get this depression by bringing the turret forward, but other factors such as the space/volume requirement for the driver and the need to provide for a reasonable slope of armour on the front glacis plate will mitigate against this.

The 180 mils depression could be relatively easily achieved by placing the trunnions fairly high, but it can be seen that recourse to such a measure will inevitably lead to a high turret roof and so the position of the trunnions becomes a matter of compromise.

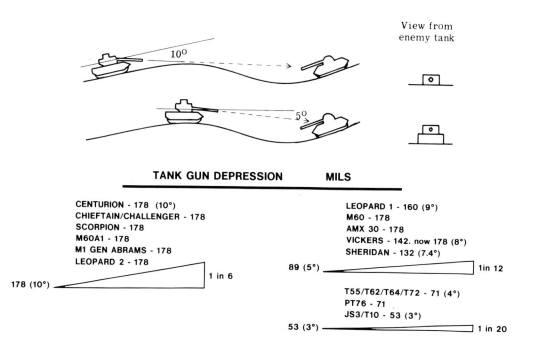

Fig. 3.2 Effect of gun depression

It must be possible to load at all angles of elevation and depression so the inboard length of the gun plus the length of the largest indivisible piece of ammunition becomes another critical factor.

It should be noted that the loading length required is not necessarily measured from the rear of the breech but from the rear of the chamber in the case of a non-tied breech block, which is the type adopted by most tank guns. It is immediately apparent that the major advantage of separate ammunition is that the longest single piece is considerably shorter than fixed ammunition. (See Fig. 3.4).

TURRET AND MANTLET

Before considering the effect on turret ring diameter it is appropriate to look at some of the factors affecting the choice of mantlets. As the gun elevates and depresse depresses it is necessary to provide the crew inside the turret with the same degree of protection as afforded by other parts of the turret within the frontal arc. It is desirable that the hole in the front is kept as small as possible and the mantlet must keep out small arms fire as well as all calibres, up to and including main calibres. Various designs of mantlets have been tried over the years with the idea of providing protection with the lightest weight and least complication, and these can generally be classified as interior or exterior mantlets. The diagrams show two classic exterior mantlet designs, with marked similarities, for the Panther (Fig. 3.3a) and the Centurion (Fig. 3.3b).

The position of the trunnions and the size and weight of the mantlet will also affect

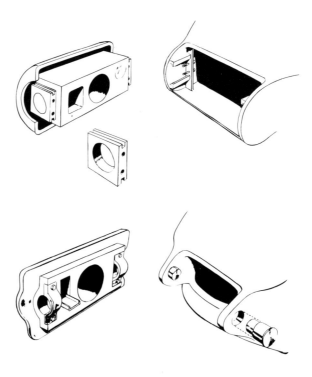

Fig. 3.3 Panther and Centurion mantlets

the turret balance. It is desirable that the turret should balance in the vertical axis about its point of rotation as this will reduce the loads on the turret traverse gear. In extreme cases where the out-of-balance forces are high and the tank is on the side slope of a hill, the traversing loads could make it difficult for the gunner to traverse the turret by hand or put very high energy demands on the power traverse.

It will also be necessary to balance the turret about a horizontal axis if undue loading on the turret ring ball race is to be avoided. One method of avoiding this is to provide the turret with a bustle. This not only helps to balance the turret but also produces a valuable space under the armour for the stowage of various items. The British Chieftain utilises this space for the stowage of projectiles, turret service batteries and the NBC filtration equipment, whilst there is a tendency in modern tanks, such as the American XM1 General Abrams and the German Leopard 2, to use the bustle as the major ammunition stowage area.

The turret, complete with gun, represents about 20% of the total weight of the tank so that mounting the turret and ensuring it can perform all its battle functions at any position and condition of movement is a complex engineering problem.

The turret ring and then its balance race must not only support the weight of the turret but it must also prevent the turret lifting off during cross-country movement when it is subject to vertical acceleration. There are also the firing stresses from the gun to be absorbed which may amount to 3-6 G depending on the propellant charge and the angle of elevation at the time of firing. All this must be achieved at minimum friction to keep the turret rotation loads at a minumum. There may be an additional requirement to provide a gas and water seal at the turret ring for NBC protection and deep wading. The production of a suitable turret ball race calls for precision engineering of the highest order and it is not uncommon for the roller or ball bearings to break up under the stain or an uneven "lumpy" ball race to develop which is sometimes called "Brinelling".

Another requirement is to provide an interface with the hull so that electrical, inter-communication and hydraulic services can pass between the turret and the hull. This is normally achieved by means of a rotary base junction containing all the necessary electrical and hydraulic slip rings. There is obviously a finite limit to the number of reliable slip rings that can be incorporated into such a device and with the continuing trend towards more and more electronic devices, methods other than elementary slip rings for direct current are required.

DIAMETER OF THE TURRET RING

We have already seen how the choice of gun affects the position of the trunnions and by reference to Fig. 3.4 it can be seen that if loading and firing at all angles of elevation are to be possible then the diameter of the turret ring is also critical. If the turret ring is to be kept within the track (Fig. 3.5a), then this immediately fixes the width of the tank, as now the overall width becomes the turret ring diameter plus the width of the two tracks. Another factor has now to be considered, as it is very desirable that the steering ratio be kept as near as possible to 1.5 and certainly below 1.8. The steering ratio or L/C ratio is defined as the ratio of the length of the track on the ground to the distance between the track centres (Fig. 3.7). If the length is increased without a corresponding increase in width, the ratio rises very sharply and in extreme cases the tank will not turn at all unless it is on a slight bump, which effectively shortens the length of the track on the ground, or unless it is on a smooth tarmac or concrete surface where the turning resistance is low. So the width of the tank must be directly related to the length of the tank.

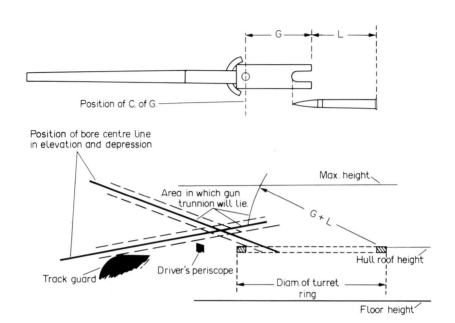

Fig. 3.4 Fitting the main armament

If we are to keep within restrictions imposed by the rail gauge and we keep the
turret ring within the inner limits of the track we would probably be limited to a
turret ring diameter of approximately 2.5 m (see Fig. 3.5a). We can increase the
turret ring diameter by building sponsons over the track and in extreme cases this
could mean that the turret ring could have a diameter almost as great as the overall
width of the tank (see Fig. 3.5b). Such a solution does mean that the sides of the
hull at that point have vertical armour, which is highly undesirable, particularly
in such a critical area. We therefore normally find that a compromise solution is
adopted whereby the turret ring is raised above the upper track level by sponsons,
which increases the overall height, but as the turret ring does not extend to the
full width of the hull it then allows for some degree of armour sloping to be adopted
(see Fig. 3.5c).

Reference to Fig. 3.7 will show how we are now developing on the diagram the
features that affect the size of the turret. In the past the thickness of armour on
the side of the turret had little or no influence on the size or interior volume of
the turret. With modern composite armours of the Chobham type the real density
of the armour is such that it may well be that the interior volume of the turret is
dictated by the rail loading gauge and the thickness/volume that the composite armour
occupies. In a modern tank with sophisticated gun fire control equipment it is proving
increasingly difficult to find sufficient space under a composite armour turret to
seat the gunner and give him the instruments and controls he needs to fight the
tank and yet maintain the width of the turret within the rail loading gauge.

When we look at the height analysis we must first of all distinguish between tactical
height and actual height. The tactical height of a tank is that part of the tank that
has to be exposed in order to engage the enemy, whereas the actual height is normally taken to be the height of the tank from the ground to the highest fixed part.
This is normally taken to be the top of the Commander's cupola, but care must always

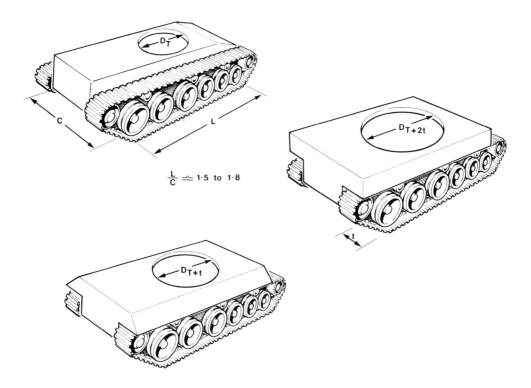

Fig. 3.5 Fitting the turret ring into the hull

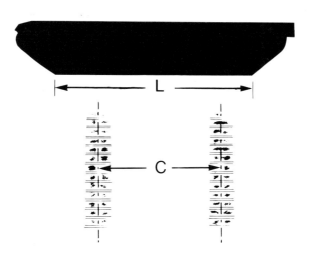

Fig. 3.6 Steering – L/C ratio

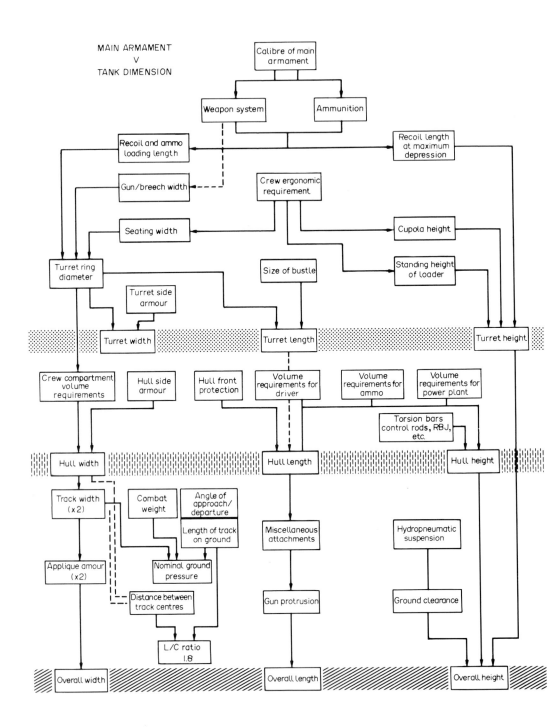

Fig. 3.7 Main armament vs. tank dimension

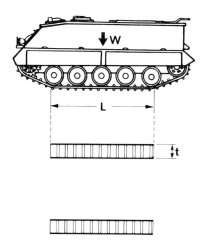

Fig. 3.8 Nominal ground pressure of tracked vehicles

be exercised when comparing the relative heights of tanks to ensure that the same datum points are used. We have already looked at the position of the gun trunnions and it is now apparent that the trunnion position has a major influence on tactical and actual height. The requirement for 180 mils depression not only raises the height of the trunnions above the turret ring in comparison with a tank requiring only 90 mils depression, but it also means that the turret roof will be higher, thus raising the actual and tactical height.

Another factor to be considered is the need for the loader to stand upright on his side of the turret whilst loading the gun. It is normal practice to provide a turret floor that rotates with the turret, and this will be a finite height above the hull floor. If we then have to allow for a standing man wearing a helmet we will need to add almost 2 m. With ammunition calibres in excess of 75 mm it is not possible for a seated loader to maintain the required rates of fire, so unless we accept the need for some selection in the size of the crew, as do the Russians, or we introduce an autoloader, then we are left with the need to accommodate a standing loader. This, or the gun depression, will fix the height of the turret roof and then it is a question of national preference what other fixtures are added. It will be necessary to fit a Commander's cupola and the height of this can vary from the low and relatively simple types of the earlier Russian tanks to the mini-turrets favoured by the Americans on the M48 and some marks of M60. A glance at Table 1 will show the very marked differences in height between the Russian and American tanks. Although this table does not show the relationship of the tactical height to the overall height, there is a direct relationship and the higher the tank the greater the target it will present to the enemy on the battlefield.

HULL DIMENSIONS

Reference in the diagram in Fig. 3.5 shows that the hull width is related to the turret ring diameter and the need to stay within the rail gauge. With some designers introducing composite armour side plates the width of the tank can be significantly larger than the distance to the outer edge of the tracks might suggest. If composite armour is so utilised, then it will probably be necessary to make special arrangements for rail movement and on Leopard 2 provision is made for the front thick side plates to lift over on hinges and lie flat on the top of the front track guards when the tank is travelling on rail flats.

The height of the hull is determined by a combination of several factors. At one time the critical factor was the need to accommodate a seated driver in an upright position, but since the innovation of a reclining driver as in the Chieftain, this has allowed the hull height to be reduced by up to 300 mm. However, with the demand for increased power/weight ratios and the restriction on the space available for the power plant (see Chapter 4), it could well be that the minimum height of the engine will be a critical factor. It is a common feature of a modern main battle tank to have the engine deck height above the level of the turret ring. This is not a tactical constraint, providing that the turret can rotate through 360° without elevating the gun unnecessarily, although it is obvious that there is little possibility of giving the gun any depression when the gun is facing to the rear.

If the tank utilises torsion bar suspension then allowance must be made for the torsion bars and their protective shields to be laid transversely across the hull floor. This can add approximately 150 mm to the height of the hull and one advantage of suspension systems contained within the track envelope such as Horstmann and hydropneumatic is that they help to keep hull height to a minimum. If we wish to stow ammunition vertically below the turret ring this could be a limiting factor, but it is most unlikely that this would be allowed to influence the hull height greatly as it is probable that the ammunition would be stowed horizontally. Other stowage areas could be found, such as in the turret bustle. Ammunition which is large enough to reach the turret ring is probably getting to the maximum handling size and must be considered for separation into two pieces.

The determination of the hull length will depend upon many things. Starting at the front there is the hull armour thickness to be considered, which may be appreciable with modern composite armours. There is also the need to accommodate the driver in a reclining position so that his periscope is still forward of the turret ring. Then there will be the swept volume required for the turret basket and turret services. The length will be at least as long as the hull is wide and may be even longer if it is decided to provide extra ammunition stowage forward of the trunnions.

Although most tanks provide limited access between the turret and the driver's compartment at certain gun positions, the engine compartment is almost invariably closed off by a bulkhead. Sometimes arrangements are made whereby the engine can aspirate through the turret, and this is particularly important if deep wading or schnorkelling is contemplated. It does, however, make it very cold for the crew! If the bulkhead is fixed at the rear of the crew compartment then the space available for the power plant is clearly defined.

The next chapter explains the need for the power plant to occupy the minimum volume, but if we remember that the width of the vehicle is in a direct relationship to the distance between the track centres we can see that the length of track on the ground is related to the turret ring diameter.

Theoretically, provided we keep the length of track in contact with the ground within these limits, then we could extend the tank or give it a larger overhang at either end without penalty. Unfortunately this is not so and there are severe limitations on the amount the tank can extend either forwards or rearwards over the normal track contact length.

The first limitation is the angle of approach and departure. If the hull protrudes beyond the track envelope in front, then the tank will have difficulty climbing banks or crossing ditches. Similarly the rear of the tank ideally should not extend beyond the rear sprocket or idler, although in practice this is not so important as the angle of approach. The relationship between the contact length and the overall length is called the pitch ratio and designers aim for a ratio of about 1.5 to 1.8. Anything above that is likely to be the major contributory factor to excessive vehicle pitching which may cause crew sickness or will certainly produce crew fatigue and could become a limiting factor on how fast the crew will tolerate the vehicle to be driven, especially in cross-country conditions.

A further effect of excessive overhang could be that the nominal ground pressure would increase as the overall weight of the tank would become greater without providing for a larger area of track in contact with the ground.

DESIGN BALANCE

One of the areas where a balance has to be struck by the designer between the various user requirements is in the relationship of the nominal ground pressure (NGP) to the L/C ratio. Nominal ground pressure is defined as:

$$\text{NGP} = \frac{\text{Vehicle weight}}{\text{area of tracks in contact with the ground}}$$

and it is either in lb/in^2 (Imp) or KPa (SI) (see Fig. 3.8).

It should be noted that this is a nominal pressure, as vehicles with very flexible tracks and few road wheels bearing on the tracks may have peak pressures under these wheels of five or six times the NGP. In extreme cases and under certain conditions these peak pressures can cause a collapse of the soil. This collapse is cumulative. As each road wheel passes it sinks further into the ground and the vehicle adopts a nose up attitude and the rear of the tank may begin to belly.

At the other end of the scale, on hard going, only the grousers or pads are in contact with the ground and this may only represent 50% of the nominal contact area. So it is only when the track has sunk about 23 mm into the ground that the actual pressure approximates to the nominal pressure.

In order to achieve a more accurate measure of the ability of vehicles to cross country, a method has been developed by the British Military Vehicles and Experimental Establishment to arrive at the mean maximum pressure (MMP). This takes into account the weight of the vehicle together with the area of track in contact with the ground, in addition to the number, size and pitch of the road wheels. It aims to average out the peak pressures under the road wheels and the minimum pressures between them. This can be closely correlated for tracked vehicles, but has yet to find international acceptance.

As one criterion on a vehicle's cross-country ability as its nominal ground pressure, it is important that this should be as low as possible. If we accept that there is a finite limit to the length of the track on the ground due to the L/C ratio requirement and maximum width of the tank, then the only possible way to improve the NGP is by either reducing the weight of the tank or increasing the area in contact with the ground by making the tracks wider. This can only be done to a limited extent on main battle tanks as excessive track width would seriously inhibit the hull width and markedly decrease the volume under armour. It also makes the tracks themselves very heavy, which increases the rolling resistance and makes it necessary for more robust and consequently heavier road wheels, top rollers and suspension. It also makes track adjustment and maintenance by the crew a heavy and tiring task.

When it is of paramount importance to have a very low nominal ground pressure, such as in over-snow vehicles, very wide, light tracks are used, but there is little available space in the hull between the tracks and all the payload is carried above the track level. This is acceptable for logistic vehicles but hardly suitable for an armoured fighting vehicle.

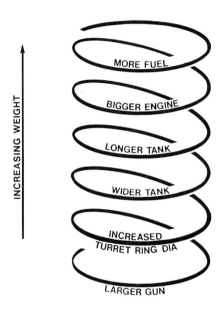

Fig. 3.9. The weight spiral

SELF TEST QUESTIONS

QUESTION 1   What are the main constraints which limit the maximum size of
              an armoured fighting vehicle?

              Answer   ....

                        ....

                        ....

QUESTION 2   If a high-velocity gun is selected, what other design problems does
              this bring in its turn?

              Answer   ....

                        ....

                        ....

QUESTION 3   Why is it important to obtain the maximum amount of gun depression?

              Answer   ....

                        ....

                        ....

QUESTION 4   What is the purpose of the mantlet and what are the two main types?

              Answer   ....

                        ....

                        ....

QUESTION 5   What is the function of the rotary base junction?

              Answer   ....

                        ....

                        ....

QUESTION 6   What is the purpose of the "bustle"?

              Answer   ....

                        ....

                        ....

                        ....

QUESTION 7   Define L/C and why is it important?

              Answer   ....

                        ....

....

QUESTION 8   What is meant by tactical height?

              Answer   ....

                        ....

                        ....

QUESTION 9   What factors determine the height of the hull?

              Answer   ....

                        ....

                        ....

                        ....

QUESTION 10   Define nominal ground pressure (NGP)

              Answer   ....

                        ....

                        ....

Answers on page 220.

4. Power Trains

REQUIREMENTS

Power trains cover the complete installation for the propulsion of any land vehicle, from the fuel tanks to the road wheels or sprockets. Major components include the engine itself, the change-speed transmission, and in the case of track-layers the steering mechanism.

Historically, the earliest practical tanks were conceived in time of war; provision of suitable engines posed a challenging problem. Aircraft engines were in critically short supply and the commercial vehicle industry not sufficiently mature to provide a source; consequently, special-to-purpose engines were developed. Throughout the subsequent three decades, however, piston aircraft engines, together with the truck, bus and car industries, provided the source. MBTs built since the mid 1940s, have had power/mass of the order 9-12 kW/tonne, giving maximum road speeds of the order 40-50 km/h. At this level, the complete power train occupies about 38% of the internal space (see Fig. 4.1), and its surrounding armour is a major contributor to the vehicle weight, more so than the power train itself. So it is important to achieve minimum bulk in the overall train, and in each of its components. Compactness is the greatest single virtue that a tank engine can have. Tanks entering service in the 1980s will have power/mass about twice as high as their predecessors, and since there is no way that the current 38% may be allowed to escalate towards 76%, marvels of compactness must be achieved. Lighter AFVs exhibit the same logic, but much less cogently. In a reconnaissance vehicle, the bulk of the crew is unlikely to be less than 75% of that in a MBT, but the total bulk may be 25% only. If crew bulk has become more significant, then power train bulk must be less so. In personnel carriers, the crew bulk is even more dominant.

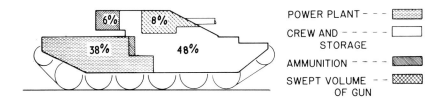

Fig. 4.1 Volumetric division of a typical battle tank

In all engine duties, compactness is desirable, but in none except the MBT is it crucial. Helicopters demand primarily high power/weight and mission reliability. Trucks are conceived around whole life costing, which leads to initial simplicity, long mean life between overhauls and extreme fuel economy; compactness has low priority. This one argument forces tank engine design ever further away from commercial practice. It is true that the situation in any one country at a particular time may appear to contravene this generalisation, but such would be a temporary and local trend only. Tank engines are "military specials". The power levels in wheeled AFVs are such that engines and change-speed gearboxes off the commercial shelf may be suitable; some manufacturers have found it possible to use commercial drive axles too. But really fast track-layers must integrate their change-speed and steering functions into one gearbox, and this too then becomes a military special.

Military vehicles cover the whole spectrum, from staff cars and low mobility trucks to MBTs. At one end, the equipment represents an almost unmodified commercial purchase; at the other, the vehicle and all its automotive components represent military specials, well removed from commercial practice.

MATCHING THE ENGINE TO THE DUTY

Resistances to Motion

When a land vehicle moves, it may encounter three types of resistive force:

> rolling resistance, air resistance and gradient resistance.

The sum of these is called the road load. To overcome them steadily, the power train must provide a driving force, the tractive effort, equal to their sum.

Rolling Resistance

Rolling resistance is encountered when a vehicle is pushed slowly over a level surface. It comes from friction in a variety of bearings and seals, rub between gear teeth, brake rub, distortion of tyres or tracks and distortion of the ground. On metalled surfaces, the last of these is negligible, and of the others, tyre/track distortion is the dominant factor for a vehicle in good condition. Under these conditions, rolling resistance in wheeled vehicles shows little speed sensitivity up to the maxima common in military vehicles, and is typically about 2–2½% of the weight. Rolling resistance so expressed, as a percentage or fraction of the weight, is called specific rolling resistance. For tracked vehicles it is typically 4–5% of the weight at low speeds, and rises towards about 8% at 80 km/h. On soft surfaces, ground distortion soon becomes dominant. Thus, even on firm turf whereon tracks just leave a neat print, about 2% is added to the values above. For ground still softer, it becomes very difficult to quantify the going type. On a ploughed field, rolling resistance can certainly be about 10% of the weight, but may range from about 8 to 18% with topsoil type, wetness and time since ploughing.

Air Resistance

Air resistance of a vehicle is governed by its frontal area, how "streamlined" its shape is, and the square of its speed through the air. For on-road vehicles, air resistance is important; at 80 km/h on the level, it represents about half of the total road load for a typical private car. Large trucks have greater resistances, but their air resistance represents a smaller proportion of the total, typically about 15%. By comparison, armoured vehicles are densely packed and slow; this makes their weight and rolling resistance dominant compared with their frontal area and air resistance. So air resistance is insignificant for AFVs.

Gradient Resistance

Gradient resistance is given by $W \sin \theta$ (see Fig. 4.2). Slopes are commonly designated in the form 1 in 5, or 20%, but this is ambiguous. It can mean either 1 up for 5 horizontal, or 1 up for 5 along the slope, giving $\theta = 11.3°$ or $11.5°$ respectively. Since metalled roads rarely exceed 1 in 3 gradient, the difference is not serious. But for steeper slopes met in off-road operation, it is safer to designate slopes by the angle θ. On this basis maximum road slopes will be about 19°.

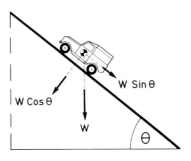

Fig. 4.2 Effect of gradient

Off-road, slopes of 30° to 40° may be encountered. Steeper slopes make resistance to motion $W \sin \theta$ greater, while grip on the ground, governed by $W \cos \theta$, lessens. On dry road, a slope of 45° is about the ultimate climbable, and this only at the expense of wheel or track slip and burned rubber. Off-road surfaces usually give less grip than road, so realistic limits for steady climb are about 28° only for all-wheel drive, and 38° for track-layers. With a flying start, steeper short slopes may be climbed. Start from rest on a slope is another matter, introducing more complex considerations of clutch or coupling capacity.

For any given vehicle type, e.g. a fast track-layer, the power/weight governs the maximum achievable road speed on level metalled surfaces. In this context, it is important to appreciate that the achievable maximum power at the road wheels or the sprockets, road power, can be much less than the manufacturer's quoted power for the bare engine. Variations in the engine test-bed procedure affect power at the flywheel; installation into a vehicle can affect power losses via filters, silencers, etc., and losses in the transmission render the road power lower still.

Constant Power Characteristic

Consider a MBT, having mass 55 tonne (weighing 540 kN), and maximum power at the sprockets of 1080 kW, i.e. power/weight of 2 kW/kN; this is rather better than the best likely to enter service in the 80s. It will probably be so geared as to be as fast as possible in high gear on a slight road upgrade; this avoids endless fussy gear changing in typical easy road running. Then it will be capable of about 80 km/h at maximum power, and probably a little more on the level or a slight downgrade as its engine runs onto its governor (Appendix A, p.77 refers).

If the going should become more difficult, due to upgrade or soft ground, the vehicle must slow down. But for optimum performance under these more arduous conditions it should still be possible to deliver 1080 kW onto the sprockets. The power train should ideally be capable of exerting its maximum power, on demand, irrespective of how fast the vehicle is moving, or of how fast its sprockets are turning. This ideal is called a constant power engine.

Thus, if this MBT should now encounter a gradient of 38°, (limit for track-slip), with going such as to give rise to specific rolling resistance of 10%, it should achieve 10 km/h thereon (Appendix A, p.77 refers). These two running conditions are shown in Fig. 4.3, plotted as specific tractive effort (tractive effort divided by weight) against road speed. All points on the curve between them represent 1080 kW. As the going worsens and the road load increases, the road speed must fall, and the resulting tractive effort increases to match the road load.

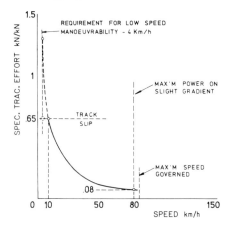

Fig. 4.3 Performance of a constant power engine

At first sight it might seem irrelevant to provide specific tractive effort greater than 0.65, since track-slip would result. However, at this condition the vehicle would still be moving at 10 km/h, and operational circumstances will arise when this is too fast, e.g. moving with walking infantry. Military vehicles need to be able to move at speeds down to 4 km/h, under the worst conditions of going, for long sustained periods, without slipping a friction clutch. To maintain such a low road speed, either a very low gear may be provided or, alternatively, a hydrokinetic coupling/converter, which by being able to slip continuously if provided with suitable cooling arrangements can allow slow movement. For further detail on this see Chapter 5.

Real Engine Characteristics

Real engines can achieve nothing like this constant power curve; in almost all of them, power will begin to drop when increased loading begins to force their speed down, even though they be drive flat-out all the time. Even when the circumstances demand something less than maximum power, piston engines cannot achieve anything like the range of speed (80 to 4 km/h) required by our hypothetical vehicle.

Figure 4.4 shows what might be expected from engines designed for MBTs.

To retain something approaching maximum power availability over the whole range of road speeds, a limit must be imposed upon the range of engine speeds to be used in flat-out driving, though in easy driving the engine can and will be taken outside this range. This is achieved by changing the gearing between the engine and the road wheels or sprockets, so that the engine may be operated fairly close to 100% speed at any vehicle road speed. How many gears will need to be provided will depend upon the engine

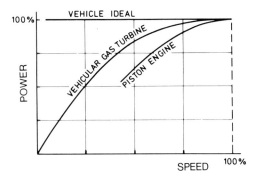

Fig. 4.4 Power/speed characteristics

characteristic, how much power drop from 100% is acceptable, how and where the vehicle is to be operated, and how much driver skill may be anticipated.

Considering the first of these, the gas turbine can have a characteristic nearer to the ideal than the piston engine, and so may need less gears. In heavy road vehicles, the acceptable power drop would be less than 20%, and with a piston engine this leads to between eight and sixteen gears. For optimum performance on paper, the MBT would need a comparable number, but this is not practicable. Already gearbox bulk is comparable with that of the engine itself and, furthermore, cross-country going changes so rapidly that the driver, or the auto-change mechanism, would continually be confronted with decisions about changing through several gears at once. So an inadequate number of gear ratios must be accepted and, as partial compensation, a very rapid, hot-shift gear-change be provided.

Fuel Consumption

So far we have talked primarily about hard driving for performance, but in practice, land vehicles spend much of their time at light loads (even negative when the vehicle overruns in engine braking). Thus, to achieve long range with minimal fuel bulk under armour, and to minimise logistic problems, low fuel consumption at all powers is desirable. Most engines certainly burn less fuel when driven softly rather than hard; but to quantify this we must consider whether the fuel consumption drops *pro rata* with the reduction of power.

Engines burn some fuel when idling, just to keep running. Fuel is then burned for zero power output; this represents zero efficiency of conversion of the fuel's energy into useful work. Thus, engines have zero efficiency at idle. Generally, their efficiency is best at or near to full power, and then gets progressively worse as their output is restricted; the relationship is not linear.

In the world of vehicle engines, it is common to talk not about efficiency, but rather about the rate of fuel consumption divided by the power. This is called specific fuel consumption, sfc, and has units of the form kg/kW h. At idle, engines burn some fuel for zero useful power; sfc is then infinite. So low efficiency implies high sfc and vice-versa.

The duty of driving a land vehicle is hard on engines. They are expected to run over a wide range of speeds, and to produce near maximum power at all of them. They must run at light loads too, and accept continual see sawing wildly over the whole range of speeds and loads. They must be economical of fuel, not only on full power but at all lighter loads too. On top of all this, they must accept mechanical shocks, as in gear changing, and thrive on maintenance standards far lower than those of the aircraft world. Tank engines in particular are built in penny numbers, and never see enough in-service running to become properly developed before they are retired as obsolete. Finally, they are expected to be relatively cheap; we do expect a lot for our money.

ENGINE TYPES

Currently available engine types for AFV propulsion include spark ignition (SI, petrol, gasoline) engines, compression ignition (CI, diesel, oil) engines and gas turbines. Steam has been considered, but the bulk of the necessary cooling system eliminates it from free-roving vehicles in general and AFVs in particular. The same appears true of the Stirling, (hot-air) engine. So we will discount both these types. SI and CI engines are usually reciprocators, but could use Wankel rotary mechanisms. As SI engines, rotaries offer commendable compactness in larger powers, though suffering real, not necessarily insuperable, problems of gas leakage;

these can lead to questionable life and inferior fuel economy. But SI engines are unattractive for future AFVs as explained below. Because of the compactness of rotary SI engines, determined efforts have been made to develop compact rotary CI engines, but the problems escalate, and these have not been successful. So we will discount rotary engines too.

SI reciprocators have been much used to power AFVs, but they have lost ground. At the powers required in small AFVs, they do have a compactness advantage over CI, but less at MBT powers where bulk is critical. Commercial expertise in high-powered engines has evaporated with the demise of big piston aircraft engines; fuel consumption is heavy compared with CI, and the volatility of the fuel gives rise to greater fire risk by accident than with diesoline, kerosene or paraffin. Since most readers will be familiar with SI engines in cars, they do provide a useful entree to studying CI performance, but the future for AFV engines does not lie with SI.

RECIPROCATING PISTON ENGINES

Four-stroke cycle

Most readers will be familiar with the mechanism inside a typical car engine and its nomenclature (see Fig. 4.5); also with the four-stroke cycle (see Fig. 4.6).

At A, the falling piston INDUCES fresh charge from the carburettor via the open inlet valve, opened by the camshaft, not shown in Fig. 4.6.

At B the rising piston COMPRESSES the charge, and near the top of this stroke, called inner dead centre or idc, the charge is sparked.

The resultant combustion increases the gas pressure inside the closed cylinder, causing EXPANSION which drives the piston down at C.

At D the rising piston EXHAUSTS the spent gases through the open exhaust valve.

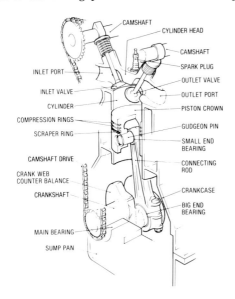

Fig. 4.5 Engine components

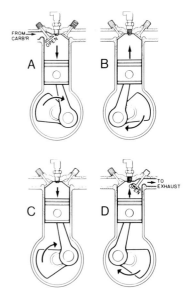

Fig. 4.6 Four-stroke cycle

SI/CI Differences

In a SI engine, the fuel and air are pre-mixed in a carburettor, and enter the cylinder as a fairly homogeneous mix. Power is controlled by a throttle, acting on both fuel and air (see Fig. 4.7). Petrol injection may be used instead of a carburettor. Usually this implies injection into the inlet manifold, upstream of the inlet valve (see Fig. 4.8). The fuel is metered by the injection system and the air by a throttle, the two controls being suitably linked. Again, the charge within the cylinder is fairly homogeneous; such a charge will burn satisfactorily over a narrow band only of air/fuel ratios, 12–17/1 by mass.

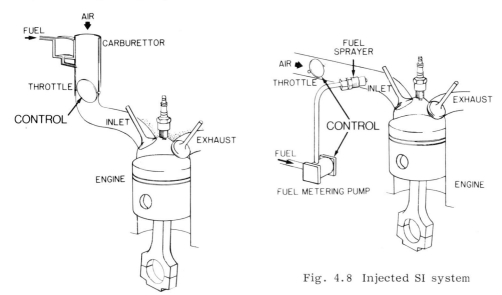

Fig. 4.8 Injected SI system

Fig. 4.7 Carburetted SI system

In a CI engine, fuel injection is directly into the combustion space, via the cylinder head (see Fig. 4.9). There is no control upon the air flow into the engine, the charge is not homogeneous, and the air/fuel ratio varies with the load, from about

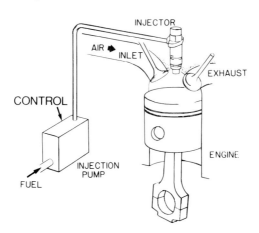

Fig. 4.9 CI system

20/1 upwards. Injection begins shortly before the piston reaches idc on the compression stroke, and ignition results from contact of the fuel with the hot air,
heated by compression. From this difference in their modes of fuel admission stem
all the main performance differences between SI and CI engines.

To ensure a high enough air temperature for compression ignition of the fuel, CI
engines need a high compression ratio, typical CR being 14–25/1. Small cylinders
suffer proportionally more heat loss from the air to the hardware and so need higher
CR. In SI engines, fuel is present throughout compression, so high CR would risk
premature ignition in part of the charge; typical CR is 8–10/1. High CR in the CI
engine leads to high pressure, heavy mechanical loading and demands heavy build.
Thus for given cylinder size, CI engines tend to be heavier than SI.

In SI engines, the fuel and air have adequate time for mixing. In CI engines,
time is limited and mixing never complete. This leads to two problems:

> Not all of the induced air can be burned. This leads to a restricted
> work output per cycle from a given cylinder size.

> Rotational speed must be kept down to maximise the mixing time.

Consequent upon less work per cycle and less cycles per second, the CI engine
is less powerful and pulls less hard than a SI engine of the same cylinder size, i.e.
has less Torque (see Fig. 4.10).

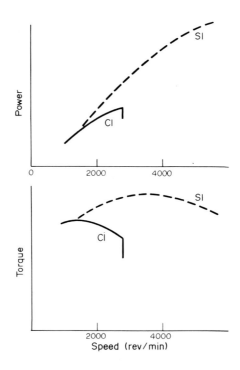

Fig. 4.10 CI and SI performance

Figure 4.11 shows the CI engine to be more economical of fuel than an equally powerful SI over the whole load range, with its proportional advantage being most marked at light loads. This economy advantage arises from two causes:

The leanness of the mixtures used in CI engines. Leanness spells economy in SI engines too, but with their homogeneous mixtures, attempts to reduce the fuel below about 80% of the correct amount lead to misfiring.

The absence of a controlling throttle in the CI air intake. Throttling a SI engine introduces a waste of work during the induction stroke (see Fig. 4.12).

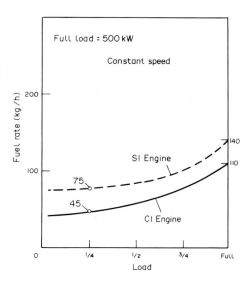

Fig. 4.11 CI and SI consumptions

The economy of CI engines has led to their general adoption in high mileage applications. These demand longevity too, and so the CI engine, with all its auxiliary equipment, is built to last and has acquired a deserved reputation for robustness in its commercial forms.

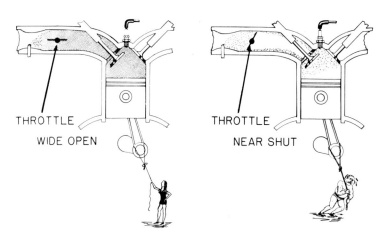

Fig. 4.12 Effect of throttling

But intrinsically it has the poorest power/bulk ratio of all the currently credible vehicle engines, in its simpler forms at least. It does not offer the compactness that is so essential a characteristic in engines for large AFVs and ways must be sought to circumvent this problem.

The reduction of fuel tankage for a mission in part offsets this, but nevertheless military engines must develop more kW from each m^3 of bulk than is commercially usual. Engines have irregular shapes, and so their bulk is difficult to quantify, but as a guide a modern truck engine achieves about 180 kW/m³, and military CI engines are in the range 600-1000kW/m³, which underlines their "special" status.

Minimising Engine Bulk

Since there is no foreseeable avenue for markedly improving the sfc of CI engines, the development of more power has to mean the burning of more fuel, and hence of air. Again, there appears little likelihood of burning the induced air more completely, so the problem reduces to increasing the air-swallowing capacity of engines without commensurate bulk increase, possibly by:

Increasing cylinder size (swept volume) within the existing bulk.

Inducing more times per second.

Filling the cylinder more completely on each cycle.

Increasing the density of the ingoing air charge.

Considering the first of these, the ratio of bulk volume/swept volume is about 100/1 in a four-stroke truck engine, and less than 50/1 in some military specials. The detail design changes leading to such compactness may militate against *in situ* maintainability, but this is not important if all maintenance is to be by removal of the complete power pack.

Considering the second, the engine might be run faster, or operate a two-stroke cycle. The former is limited in CI engines by smokey combustion and offers little gain. At given rotational speed, a two-stroke does cycle twice as frequently as a four-stroke, and this may offer some advantage in power/swept volume. But the need for a scavenge blower makes their ratio of bulk volume/swept volume high, and in the limit they are less well able to accept pressure charging than four-strokes (see below). So at the very highest ratings, two-stroke bulks compare unfavourably with four-strokes in vehicular powers.

Considering the third, the use of many individually small cylinders, with tuned inlet/exhaust systems, along with valve timings accented towards high-speed performance can give a high-power/swept volume; racing-car engines exemplify this approach. But the resulting tendency towards a narrow operating speed range is ill-suited to a vehicle requiring a wide range of road speeds and having an inadequate number of gears.

PRESSURE CHARGING AND TURBOCHARGING

This leaves us with the fourth option. A compressor may be used to drive more charge into the engine, pressure charging; engines not so equipped are naturally aspirated. Such a compressor must be driven; the power for this may come from the engine crankshaft, mechanical supercharge, or from a turbine in the engine exhaust stream, turbocharge (see Figs. 4.13 and 4.14).

In either case, the temperature as well as the pressure of the charge will be increased, and this is undesirable. It reduces the density increase achieved, and aggravates the stress level inside the engine. So a charge cooler may be fitted, cooling the heated charge either via the engine's cooling system or via atmospheric air. The former is more compact, but can cool the charge down to perhaps 100°C only. Air-to-air charge coolers can be bulky, as much as half as big as the engine radiators. But they can get the charge cooler, down to near atmospheric temperature.

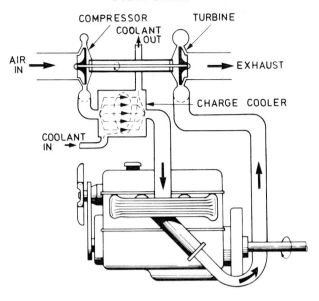

Fig. 4.13 Turbocharged system

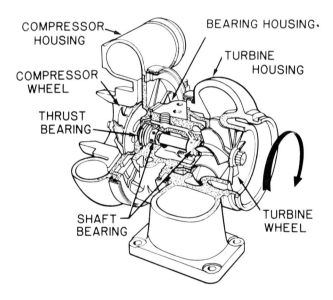

Fig. 4.14 Turbocharger

Torque/Speed and Response Lag

Pressure charging aims for increase of power, not of efficiency. Turbocharging
has small effect only upon efficiency, and this can go either way. Supercharging
is intrinsically less efficient than turbocharging, because the compressor absorbs
some of the useful engine power increase. This is particularly true at high-speed,
light load conditions, when a mechanically driven compressor may absorb nearly as

much power as at full load. Figure 4.15 illustrates the difference in fuel consumptions.

But a disadvantage for turbocharging arises in the shape of engine power/ speed characteristic to which it leads. It usually provides most power increase at high engine speed, resulting in an engine which does not pull well at low speed. Furthermore, at light engine load the turbocharger speed drops, and must rise again before the engine can accept full load; this leads to a lag in responding to sudden demands for increased power.

If at the design stage smaller nozzles are fitted in the turbine housing, the gas flow is impeded and the pressure drop increased. So more power is taken from the gases, and the turbocharger is driven faster, giving more boost at all engine speeds. In the mid-speed range, power may now be satisfactory, but at high engine speed the engine may be over-boosted or the turbocharger over-speeded to destruction. To prevent this, a valve, wastegate, may be opened automatically as boost pressure rises too high, allowing some of the exhaust to bypass the turbine

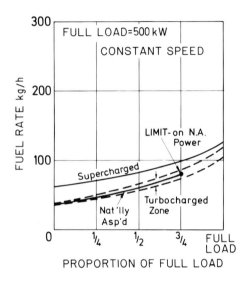

Fig. 4.15 Comparison of fuel rates

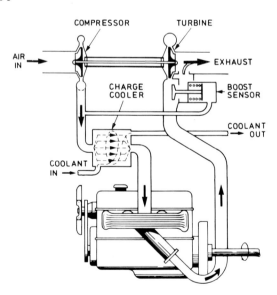

Fig. 4.16 Wastegate control

(see Fig. 4.16). This is one of several techniques for modifying the intrinsic power/ speed curve of turbocharged engines to make it more suited to automotive use.

Stress Problems in Pressure Charged Engines

To achieve compactness, most MBT CI engines are fiercely boosted, well beyond the usual limits of commercial engine practice. This leads to both mechanical stressing within the engine, blowing it apart, and thermal stressing, burning/melting it. The designer must use all his skills to avoid trouble, including better detail design of cylinder head to cylinder joints, better layout of the internal cooling circuits, better materials in valves and piston crowns, oil cooling of the pistons, and charge cooling. But ultimately he has one card only left; he must lower the compression ratio within the engine.

In a hot, loaded engine, a compression ratio much lower than normal will ensure compression ignition; but low CR will introduce problems at cold start, and perhaps at sustained idle. To cater for these conditions, artificial charge warming may be necessary. There are at least four schemes for meeting this problem.

The first requires that the CR be continuously adjustable while the engine is running – high for start and low on heavy load. This can be accomplished by a special piston having two parts – a carrier attached to the con-rod in the usual way, and a shell bearing the piston crown and the rings (see Fig. 4.17). The shell has a limited travel up and down relative to the carrier; so when it moves up, the crown moves further into the cylinder at idc, giving high CR and vice-versa. This movement between the two piston parts is controlled by pumping oil in/out of two chambers between them. Typically it can control CR between about 8/1 and 16/1.

The other three schemes all build the engine with a fixed, low CR, and then provide for artificially warming the ingoing charge at start and idle as necessary.

The second scheme achieves this by spraying fuel into the ingoing air charge and igniting it electrically if engine temperatures are low enough to make compression ignition uncertain (see Fig. 4.18). At high load conditions, this extra fuelling would be automatically turned off.

Figure 4.19 shows the third scheme, Hyperbar. Some of the air from the compressor is allowed to bypass the engine via an auxiliary combustion chamber. When this is fired, the turbine receives more energy and drives the compressor faster, so achieving more boost and a hotter charge. By tailoring the amount of bypass combustion, it may be possible to provide the preferred amount of boost at all engine speeds and loads, and so an attractive power/speed characteristic for vehicle drive. Also it maintains high

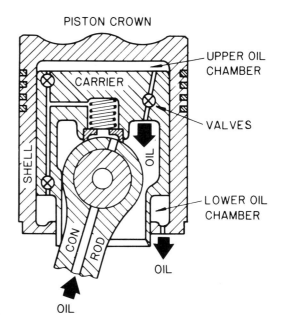

Fig. 4.17 Variable CR piston

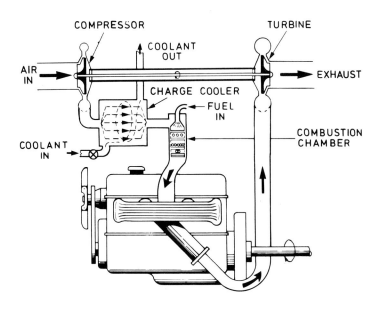

Fig. 4.18 Manifold heating

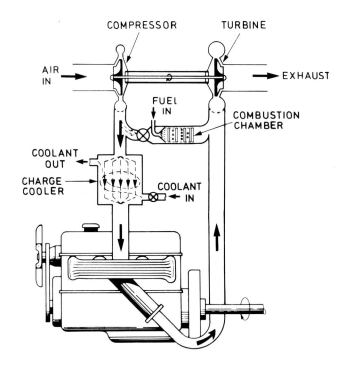

Fig. 4.19 Hyperbar system

compressor speed when the engine load is light, to achieve warm charge, and this helps to avoid the problem of response lag in accepting sudden power demands.

Figure 4.20 shows the fourth scheme which allows some of the hot exhaust gas to recirculate into the engine intake. Clearly this can maintain light load running indefinitely, but the achieving of cold start is less obvious. This is done by advancing the valve-timing of the engine during cranking. As a result, the not-yet-firing engine compresses its air charge on the compression stroke more than it expands it during expansion; so it pumps hot air back into its own inlet.

Three at least of these schemes are currently running in AFVs under development, but as yet the commercial vehicle world shows little more than polite interest in them. This highlights the gulf between commercial practice and military special engines.

Overall, the CI engine is a proven credible propulsion unit for AFVs, with known characteristics. Its greatest intrinsic weakness is its bulk, which does remain a problem despite remarkable advances. The future for it must rest with ever more intense pressure charging, leading perhaps to a "combination" with the gas turbine.

GAS TURBINES

Components and Characteristics

In a piston engine, compression, combustion and expansion follow one another sequentially in the same space; in a gas turbine, all three proceed continuously

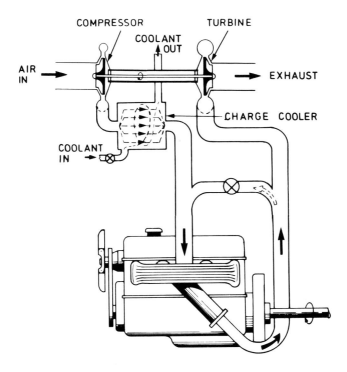

Fig. 4.20 Exhaust recirculation

and concurrently in different parts of the mechanism. This demands a separate
compressor, combustion chamber and turbine (see Fig. 4.21). The compressor
and turbine may be radial flow machines,
as in the turbocharger of Fig. 4.14, or
axial flow (see Fig. 4.22). This shows
an axial compressor; an axial turbine
looks superficially similar, but is likely
to have far fewer rows of blades.

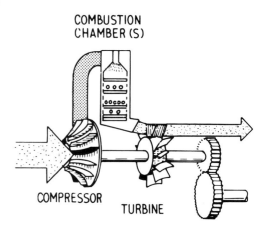

Conceptually such a machine is simple;
in reality it is much more difficult
to ensure an excess of expansive, turbine, power over compressive power
in this system than in a piston engine.
So this engine type is very sensitive
to design deficiencies and adverse
environmental conditions. Because
there are no valves, the flow is continuous and so the throughput is
large in relation to engine bulk.
Throughput relates to work output,
and so this engine is compact for its
power. Again, no valves means no

Fig. 4.21 Single-shaft gas turbine

rise of pressure in combustion, unlike the piston engine. The maximum pressure
in the engine is that achieved by compression only and so the construction is
light by comparison with piston engines; thus it is a light engine for its power.

Because the gas flow and combustion are continuous, some of the hardware
must experience temperatures comparable with the maximum gas temperature;
in an intermittently firing piston engine, hardware temperatures are much
less than gas maximum temperatures. Current blade materials restrict
gas turbine temperatures to around 1350 K, about half of the piston
engine value. The fuels burned are similar and so the air/fuel ratio must

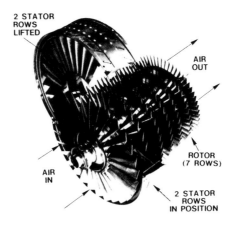

Fig. 4.22 Axial compressor

be much leaner in a gas turbine, typically about 55/1 compared with 20/1 in a CI engine. So the air throughput is large for a given power. This, taken with the sensitivity to adverse conditions, leads to bulky, low-pressure loss, air filters and inlet/exhaust ducting. But being internally aircooled, the gas turbine does not need the external cooling system that is associated with piston engines.

Twin-shaft Engines

If loading should cause the output speed of a piston engine to slow, the compression achieved is not affected; it is a function of the geometric build of the engine. But with the aerodynamic compressors used in turbochargers and gas turbines, the compression is very speed sensitive and so, if the compressor and output shafts are mechanically linked, a slowed output will lead to loss of compression. This makes the cycle ineffective, and so the output power of an engine of the type shown in Fig. 4.21 decays steeply if speed is forced down, as shown in Fig. 4.23.

But if the single turbine be replaced by two mechanically independent ones, of which the first, high pressure, drives the compressor only, and the second, low pressure, the load (see Fig. 4.24) the power/speed characteristic is changed. Even if the output is loaded until it stalls, the compressor, or gas-generator, turbine can continue to run with speed only slightly reduced, providing an effective gas cycle; so the power is well maintained with falling speed (see Fig. 4.23). Such a two-shaft engine has a power/speed characteristic automotively superior to that of a piston engine, and it is on

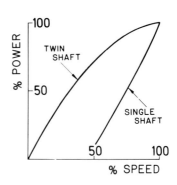

Fig. 4.23 Power/speed curves

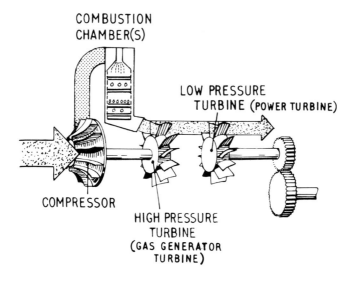

Fig. 4.24 Twin-shaft gas turbine

this system that most automotive turbines are based.

Simple gas turbines can offer extreme compactness and lightness as bare engines. Their associated gas ducting and filters are bulkier than for piston engines, but this is more than offset by their freedom from an external engine cooling system and its associated cooling drive power. In two-shaft form they have an attractive power/speed characteristic, and having no pistons are relatively free from rubbing friction. So they are easy to crank at low temperatures and can have good cold-starting capability. Because their combustion is continuous, they are tolerant of a much wider range of fuels than either SI or CI engines.

But their greatest drawback rests in their fuel consumption. At all load levels they are thirstier than piston engines of the same power, but this is particularly so at low loads. In the quarter power region, where land vehicles spend much of their operating time, simple gas turbines are as much as three times as thirsty as CI engines of equal power. This is shown in Fig. 4.25.

Heat Exchange

In the aircraft world, economy at near full load is the requirement, and this is met by engines combining a high pressure ratio with the highest gas temperatures that materials tech- nology will allow; these are outside our interest. To achieve part-load economy as well, a different approach is necessary.

An inefficient engine must rid itself of its fuel energy somehow, either to its coolant or its exhaust. Gas turbines have no cooling system, so inefficiency reflects in a hot exhaust. If this energy be used to provide some part of the heating process after the compressor, the heating to be accomplished by the fuel is reduced, and hence the fuel consumption too. This is called heat exchange (see Fig. 4.26).

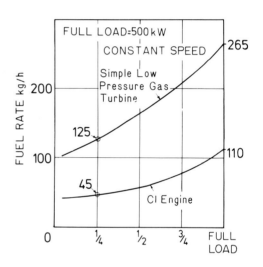

Fig. 4.25 Comparative fuel consumptions

The warm air from the compressor is heated by contact with the hot exhaust from the turbines. A heat exchanger can be in either of two forms, a recuperator or a regenerator. The former has no moving parts; a car radiator provides an example of a hot-water-to-air recuperator, and it is easy to conceive a similar device working with hot exhaust gas and compressed air. Regenerators do have moving parts (see Fig. 4.27). A disc(s), porous to air and gas flows is positioned with one edge in the warm air, the other in the hot gas, and rotated slowly. The disc material is continuously heated by the hot exhaust, and then moves into the air stream, where it gives up its heat to the warm air.

Both of these systems have their pros and cons, and there is not yet enough practical experience of either in the gas turbine field to make firm choice between them. Recuperators tend to be bulky and difficult to keep clean in prolonged service. Regenerator materials must withstand continuous cycling, hot, then cold; ceramics are preferred. Rubbing seals must be provided over their surfaces to prevent the

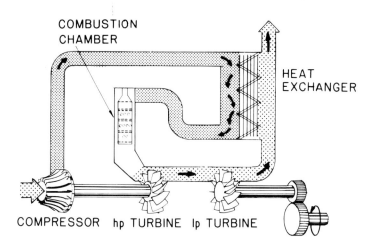

Fig. 4.26 Recuperative gas turbine

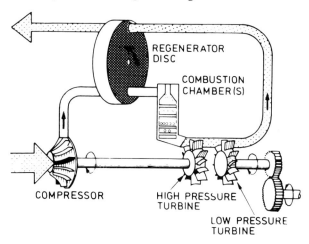

Fig. 4.27 Regenerative gas turbine

compressed air escaping directly into the exhaust ducts at atmospheric pressure. In practice, either sort of heat exchanger tends to rob the simple gas turbine of much of its compactness.

Variable Geometry

High gas turbine efficiency is dependent upon running with the highest possible gas temperature in the cycle. Much development effort has gone into developing the metal alloys currently available to withstand this, and continues to go into the development of viable ceramic components which will allow still higher temperatures. But inevitably, when an engine is driven lightly, the fuel input is reduced and consequently the top temperature tends to fall, with adverse effect on part-load economy. Recovery of waste heat via heat exchange certainly helps, but what is really wanted at part-load is a smaller engine, which may then continue to be driven flat-out, with high temperature and high efficiency.

Alternatively it might be possible to adjust the "size" of the engine while it is running; the technology for doing this is called variable geometry (see Fig. 4.28). Most automotive gas turbines include this system on their second, lp or free power turbine.

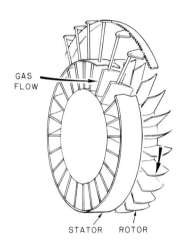

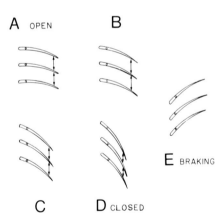

Fig. 4.28 Variable geometry

In an axial turbine comprising one row each of stator and rotor blades, the stator blades are individually pivotted, their movements being geared together. As they pivot, the gas flow passage between them reduces from A through to D, effectively making the turbine "smaller". They are programmed to do this as the load is reduced and so, as the fuel flow is cut back, the air flow reduces too. So the gas temperature falls less than it would in an engine having fixed geometry; this helps to maintain good part-load economy. Furthermore, if the blades be pivotted round to position E, they tend to blow the rotor round backwards; this provides engine braking, otherwise lacking from gas turbines.

State of the Art

Most vehicular gas turbine prototypes incorporate heat exchange plus variable geometry on their power turbine at least. But currently they still cannot match the economy of a CI engine, as shown in Fig. 4.29. So it is still not possible to buy such an engine commercially.

But for propelling a MBT, economy is less important than compactness, and the Americans have decided upon a gas turbine in their M-1 or General Abrams vehicle. This engine incorporates both a recuperator and variable geometry, and is by any standards a sensationally compact unit. The bare engine has bulk of about 1000 kW/m³ compared with best CI military special values of about 800 kW/m³; furthermore, it does not incur the bulk of an external engine cooling system, nor the associated power loss to fan drives (8–10% of the bare engine power in a CI installation). But it remains thirstier than a CI engine, and when the bulk of a complete power train, including the fuel for a mission, is assessed, the choice becomes unclear. At the present state of the art, the case for the gas turbine versus the CI engine in MBTs is arguable. Any fundamental difference is small enough to be subordinate to the development excellence of particular designs.

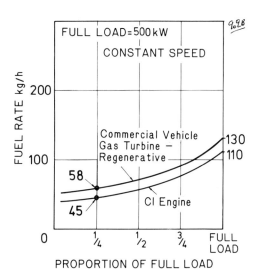

Fig. 4.29 Fuel consumption rates

Overall, the technology of gas turbines is based in the aircraft world, whereas the development of piston engines tends to be centred in the ground vehicle industry. With present-day technology, it is true that gas turbines are intrinsically more expensive to manufacture, but no less important is the fact that the staff involved in their development have for the most part aircraft industry background, and as a result a quite different order of cost-consciousness. An engine of any technical type from such a background will be expensive.

Power-for-power, aircraft industry based gas turbines cost about five times as much as standard commercial vehicle CI engines; limited production military special CI engines cost about two to two-and-half times as much as their commercial counterparts. Commercial CI engines in their turn are about five times as expensive as car SI engines on a power-for-power basis. These cost differences reflect not only the differing degrees of complexity and differing standards of manufacture, but also the different numbers of units produced in each type.

Large military engines have to be "specials", as we have stressed, but the cost of their procurement is high. Differences of detail design from commercial engines we must have, but we just cannot afford to embark upon the development of engines conceptually different from those developed for commercial roles.

FUTURE ENGINES

Adiabatic and Compound Engines

There remains considerable development potential in both the gas turbine and the CI engine. For the former, the key to further progress lies almost certainly in the development of ceramic components for the combustion chamber and the turbine. These, by allowing operation at higher temperatures than metals, will lead to improved engine efficiencies and hence lower fuel consumptions. The use of similar materials in a CI engine might allow it to dispense with some or all of its cooling system: the resulting engine is called an adiabatic engine. By itself, this would not make the engine much more efficient; most of the heat saved from the coolant would come out not as extra work, but as a hotter exhaust. It would, however, save on cooling system bulk and fan drive power, and allow the engine to accept more boosting.

As CI engines are turbocharged more intensely, the available turbine power from the exhaust gases begins to exceed markedly the power needed to drive the compressor. Even at current boost levels, it may be found necessary to jettison exhaust energy at the higher engine speeds via a waste-gate to keep the engine out of trouble. As engines capable of withstanding higher boosts are developed, it may prove viable to extract all the energy available in the exhaust and, having taken that part necessary for driving the compressor, feed the rest into the output shaft − a compound engine, as shown in Fig. 4.30.

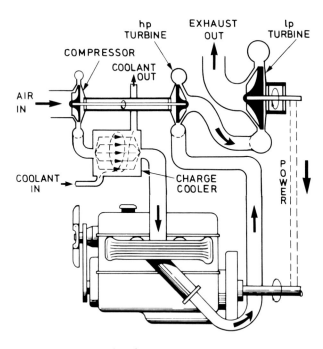

Fig. 4.30 Piston-turbo compound

This concept is not new, but it does now seem to be nearing commercial viability. The idea lends itself to combination with the adiabatic engine; for then, the extra exhaust gas energy delivered by the latter could be recouped by the turbine(s). Fully developed, such an engine ought to have a specific fuel consumption about 18% lower than that of the best current CI engines. Indeed, it represents about the most economical engine concept at vehicular powers that is conceivable within the framework of our present technology. Furthermore, it should show bulks better than the best current CI values, and approaching those of gas turbines. But its appearance should not be anticipated much before the last few years of the present century.

The future for propelling military ground vehicles lies with IC engines, be they pressure-charged piston engines, gas turbines or compounds. Fossil oil will run out, but we have the technology to synthesise substitutes; it is only a matter of when it becomes economic to do so.

APPENDIX A. ANALYTICAL EXAMPLES

On earth, 1 kg mass weighs 9.81 kN force (weight). It weighs less on the moon, because the gravitational pull is less - about 1.5 kN.

Thus, a MBT having mass 55 tonnes (see page 57) weights 540 kN.

From experience, power/weight of 2 kW/kN (see page 57) implies a maximum road speed of about 80 km/h; at this speed, specific rolling resistance on road is about 8% (see page 56).

Thus: Rolling resistance = W × Sp. RR = 540 kN × 0.08 = 43.2 kN.

For an AFV, air resistance is negligible (see page 57).

On a slight road upgrade, say 1 in 100 or 0.57°:

        Gradient resistance = W sin θ = 540 kN × 0.01 = 5.4 kN.

Thus: Road load = Rolling + Air + Gradient resistance = 48.6 kN

and: Tractive effort = Road load . . . to maintain steady motion.

Now: Road power = Tractive effort × Road speed

and: Given road power is 1080 kW (see page 57)

where: 1 kW = 1 kN m/s so Road power = 1080 kN m/s.

Then: 1080 kN m/s = 48.6 kN × Road speed

giving: Road speed at maximum power in high gear = 22.2 m/s

where: 1 m/s = 3.6 km/h so:

        Road speed at maximum power in high gear = 80 km/h.

For the same vehicle on a 38° upgrade with Sp. rolling resistance of 10%:

        Road load = 540 kN × (sin 38° + 0.1) = 386 kN.

Thus: Road speed at maximum power in low gear

            = 1080 kN m/s ÷ 386 kN = 2.8 m/s

and since maximum engine power coincides with maximum engine speed:

            Maximum road speed in low gear = 2.8 m/s = 10 km/h.

Referring to Fig. 4.11, what is the sfc of the CI engine thereon, at full power of 500 kW, and at quarter power? A larger CI engine, of maximum power 1500 kW, has the same sfcs as the engine of Fig. 4.11; what would be its rate of fuel consumption at full power?

            Refer Fig. 4.11:   Fuel rate at 500 kW = 110 kg/h.

            Whence: sfc = 110 kg/h ÷ 500 kW = 0.22 kg/kW h.

            Similarly at quarter power: sfc = 0.36 kg/kW h.

            For 1500 kW engine with sfc 0.22 kg/kW h:

                                    Fuel consumption = 330 kg/h.

SELF TEST QUESTIONS

QUESTION 1   An injector is removed from one cylinder of a four-stroke CI engine,
              and the hole left covered by a piece of cigarette paper. The engine
              is now cranked, very slowly. On which stroke(s) will the paper
              be drawn into the hole?

              Answer   ....

                        ....

                        ....

                        ....

                        ....

                        ....

QUESTION 2   For a given fuel, an air mass of 15 times the fuel mass is required
              for complete and correct combustion. Does a fuel-rich mixture have
              A/F of more or less than 15/1?

              Answer   ....

QUESTION 3   Two CI engines both have CR of 15/1. The individual cylinders
              in one engine have $\frac{1}{2}$ litre capacity, and in the other 2 litre. Which
              engine is likely to be the better cold starter?

              Answer   ....

                        ....

                        ....

QUESTION 4   Under what driving condition will a diesel engine "rev" fastest? Why
              do most diesels have governors, when most petrol engines do not?

              Answer   ....

                        ....

                        ....

                        ....

                        ....

                        ....

QUESTION 5   It is decided to turbocharge an existing CI engine, raising the intake
              pressure from 1 atm to 1.25 atm. Will the power increase be 25%,
              less or more?

              Answer   ....

                        ....

. . . .

. . . .

QUESTION 6   Waste-gates are now widely used on the turbochargers of diesel-
              engined road vehicles, but they are even more essential on petrol-
              engined road vehicles. Explain.

              Answer   . . . .

                        . . . .

                        . . . .

                        . . . .

                        . . . .

                        . . . .

                        . . . .

QUESTION 7   At Fig. 4.31 is a proposal for a modified gas turbine cycle, intended
              particularly for military use. It is claimed that by exposing the
              exhaust gases, via the regenerator, to the cold intake air, they
              would be well cooled, leading to less thermal signature from the
              vehicle. At the same time, because the exhaust would be better
              cooled than in a conventional heat-exchange cycle, less heat would
              be wasted to exhaust and so the cycle efficiency and the vehicle
              fuel consumption should both be improved. Comment.

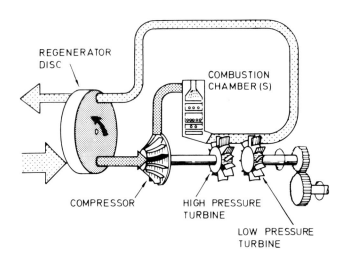

Fig. 4.31 Proposed gas turbine

              Answer   . . . .

                        . . . .

                        . . . .

....

....

....

QUESTION 8   The high-pressure ratio gas turbines used in modern helicopters do not use heat exchangers; one obvious reason is the weight and bulk of such devices. But there is another, more fundamental, reason. Explain.

Answer   ....

....

....

....

QUESTION 9   The MBT of Appendix A is required to climb a slope of 8° on going with specific rolling resistance of 8%. With ideally chosen gearing, how fast could it be?

Answer   ....

....

....

....

....

....

....

QUESTION 10   The CI powered MBT of Appendix A has transmission efficiency of 72%. What must be its engine power at the flywheel? At all percentage loads, this CI engine has the same sfcs as that of Fig. 4.11. If a battlefield day may be represented by 10 h continuous running at 1/4 full load, what mass of fuel must be carried? Diesoline has density 0.84 kg/litre; what volume has this fuel? Repeat these calculations for a gas turbine powered variant of the vehicle. Maximum power is unchanged; the sfc of the gas turbine may be found from Fig. 4.29; the density of gas turbine fuel is 0.74 kg/litre.

Answer   ....

....

....

....

....

. . . .

. . . .

. . . .

. . . .

Answers on page 221.

5. Transmissions

REQUIREMENTS

Chapter 4 covered the engine as part of the power train. This chapter will deal with the drive-line, which distributes the engine's power to the road wheels or sprockets, modifying the torque/speed characteristic as necessary to match the engine output to vehicle demand. Major sub-systems in the drive-line include:

Change-speed gearboxes; clutches, couplings and converters; universal and constant velocity joints; differentials; steering systems for tracked vehicles.

As the nature of the ground and the gradient vary, the speed of a land vehicle must vary, even if it be driven flat-out all the time. So we would wish that the complete power train should be able to develop its maximum power, on demand, at any output speed over a wide range of speeds, a constant power engine. All real engines fail to achieve this aim, as explained in Chapter 4 (see also Fig. 5.1).

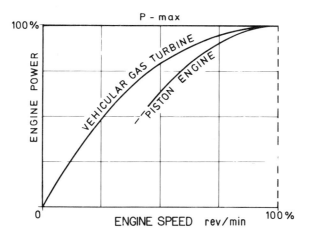

Fig. 5.1 Vehicle and engine performances

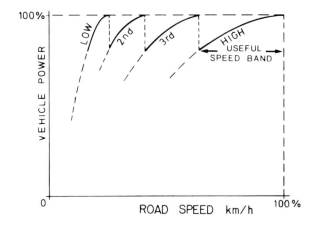

Fig. 5.2 Four gears

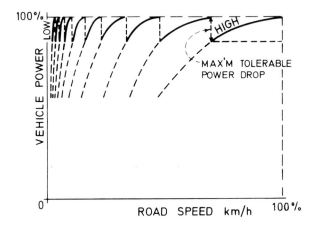

Fig. 5.3 Ten gears

So, the drive-line must provide the facility to keep the engine speed within a narrow range, not too far from the speed for maximum power, over a wide range of vehicle speeds. Changing gear achieves just this. Figure 5.2 shows how a four-speed gearbox, typical of car practice, limits the range of speeds over which the engine has to operate; it remains perfectly possible for the driver to operate the engine outside this limited range, if the circumstances demand nothing like maximum power; but he can get near maximum power if and when he needs it.

Some other vehicle might require a much wider range of road speeds. Then, more gears would become desirable; Fig. 5.3 illustrates the provision of ten forward gears. Again, if the vehicle should have a poor power/weight, then the designer may feel it necessary to enable the driver to keep the engine running condition closer to the maximum power speed than would be the case in a car; more than four forward gears would result.

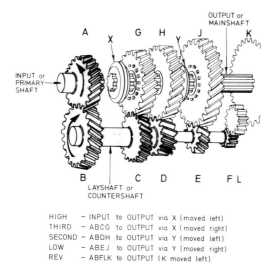

HIGH   – INPUT to OUTPUT via X (moved left)
THIRD   – ABCG to OUTPUT via X (moved right)
SECOND – ABDH to OUTPUT via Y (moved left)
LOW   – ABEJ to OUTPUT via Y (moved right)
REV   – ABFLK to OUTPUT (K moved left)

Fig. 5.4 Four-speed spur gearbox

CHANGE-SPEED GEARBOXES

The commonest form of gearbox employs spur gears, as shown in Fig. 5.4. The gears may have straight-cut teeth, as on pair F-L, single helical teeth, as on the other pairs illustrated, or double helical teeth, not shown. Straight-cut gears are cheap but noisy. Single helicals are quiet, but develop big end-wise thrusts. Double helicals are quiet and thrust-free but expensive.

In the layout shown, power enters from the left, transfers down to the counter or lay shaft via gears A-B and leaves at the end remote from the input. Such a layout is ideally suited to a vehicle having front engine and rear-wheel drive. In other vehicles, transverse engined front-wheel drive, for example, it may be convenient to take the output from the centre of the second shaft. Such a gearbox does not really have an idle or lay shaft, but the term 'layshaft gearbox' is widely used to describe all spur gearboxes.

The gear pairs C-G, D-H and E-J run together continuously, constant mesh gears. Gear K is shown out-of-mesh with L; it has to be slid along the splines on the output shaft for engagement, sliding mesh gear. The constant mesh gears on the output shaft turn continuously, but transmit drive to the shaft only when the relevant dog-clutch X or Y is engaged. Figure 5.4 shows the engagement schedule. It is impossible to run with two different gears solidly engaged at once. So there has to be a short, but finite, interruption of the power flow while gears are being changed. As a new gear is engaged, the speeds of the components to be meshed will need to be matched. To make this easy, one end of the gearbox is disconnected, usually the input end, by means of a clutch. This is necessary for starting from rest too. The speeds can be adjusted, by driver skill or by small friction clutches, not shown, inside X and Y, synchromesh. There is also real current interest in adjusting the gear speeds by electronic control of the engine speed, with clutch engaged; this is not in general use yet.

In high gear, the gearbox of Fig 5.4 will rotate its output at the same speed as its input, direct drive. If gear C were given more teeth, and gear G less, they could drive the output faster than the input; this is overdrive. It allows fast, relaxed road running at low engine speed, which is conducive to good fuel economy.

Most automatic gearboxes are based upon epicyclic gear trains, as shown in Fig. 5.5. If the sun be driven, and a load resists the carrier, the annulus will spin idly and no power is transmitted. But if now the annulus be locked, by some sort of friction brake or clutch, the carrier will be driven positively against the load, more slowly than the sun.

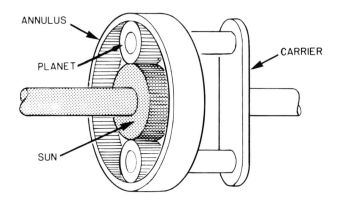

Fig. 5.5 Simple epicyclic

Alternatively, the sun and carrier could be clutched together. Then the output would be driven positively at input speed. So this one gearset can offer two output speeds for one given input speed. If the output from its carrier were to be used as the input to the sun of a second epicyclic, a choice of four output speeds could result from just two gearsets.

Such a system promises compactness. Furthermore, gear changing does not demand accurate speed adjustments on intermeshing teeth; the change can be "soft" and easy to manage, automatically if so required. Additionally, it is possible to begin the engagement of a new gear ratio before the one previously in use is completely released. This allows the transmission of some, not all, of the engine power throughout the duration of a change, referred to as hot shift. This point is very valuable in a vehicle experiencing high, off-road road loads. For in the very low gear then necessary, the range of road speeds attainable is very small, and if power is lost during a change, the vehicle may slow to such an extent that selection of the next gear becomes impossible. The drawback of epicyclic boxes lies in their power losses. Four speeds from two epicyclics would need four clutches. Two would be nominally disengaged, but incurring some rubbing losses. In complex epicyclic gearboxes, these losses, together with those from a large number of idling gears, can approach 20% of the input power.

CLUTCHES, COUPLINGS AND CONVERTERS

Friction Clutches

When starting from rest, drive interruption is necessary between the engine and the gearbox. Most commonly, this is achieved by the use of a friction clutch, directly under driver control. Figure 5.6 shows the layout of a typical clutch for light vehicle duty.

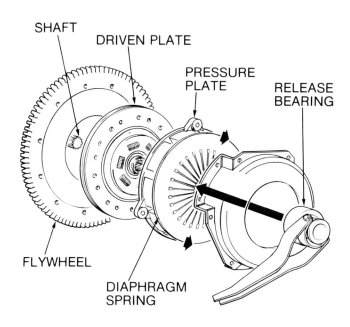

SHAFT

DRIVEN PLATE

PRESSURE
PLATE

RELEASE
BEARING

FLYWHEEL

DIAPHRAGM
SPRING

Fig. 5.6 Friction clutch

The driven plate is splined to a shaft which drives into the gearbox. The drive
comes from the engine flywheel and is passed by friction into the driven plate. To
maintain this friction, the driven plate is sandwiched between the flywheel and the
pressure plate, the latter being pressed to the left by the diaphragm spring. To
release the clutch, the driver presses the release bearing to the left. Leftwards
movement of the inner radius of the spring causes its outer radius to flex to the
right, taking the pressure off the pressure plate and the driven plate. The connection between the driver's foot and the release bearing may be achieved mechanically or hydraulically.

Fully engaged, such a clutch transmits power with near 100% efficiency; the engine
torque, or pulling effort, too is transmitted unchanged. When the clutch slips,
the output speed and power are lessened. But the transmitted torque is unchanged.
Clutches are not torque-converters.

Centrifugal Clutches

In some vehicles, a friction clutch is controlled automatically, rather than by the
driver; British Chieftain and Scorpion are examples. The friction material is
arranged as the outside of a cylinder, split axially into a series of sectors. These
are driven by the engine, and restrained from flying outwards centrifugally by
springs. But as engine speed rises, the springs are overcome, and the friction
surfaces move out, into contact with the inside of a surrounding drum, which they
then drive. So the clutch is free at engine idle speeds, but engages progressively
as the speed rises. Because the driver cannot "pre-rev" the engine, before the
clutch begins to engage, ultimate starting ability on gradients is restricted by
this system. But in any case the current trend is towards the use of a hydrokinetic coupling or coupling/converter between the engine and the gearbox.

Hydrokinetic Couplings and Converters

In a hydrokinetic coupling, or fluid flywheel, the engine drives a vaned wheel, the pump, which in turn gives whirling motion to oil; the moving oil then impinges on another vaned wheel, the turbine, and drives it. The layout and parts are shown in Figs. 5.7 and 5.8. At idle engine speeds, this effect will be insufficient to drive the output and the vehicle, but as the driver accelerates the engine, the drive will be smoothly taken up.

The torque (turning effect) taken from the oil by the output is equal and opposite to that provided by the input. Were this not so, the oil would accelerate until it was. But the output speed will be less than the input speed; there is slip. As speed rises, the slip reduces, but output power is always less than input power and the difference appears as heat in the oil. But unlike the friction material in the plate of a clutch, the oil may be readily cooled externally; so prolonged heavy slipping can be made acceptable.

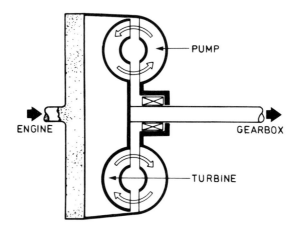

Fig. 5.7 Hydrokinetic coupling
(schematic)

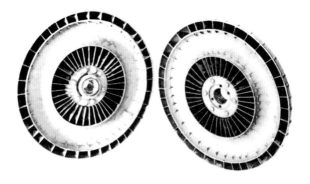

Fig. 5.8 Hydrokinetic coupling (photo)

In a converter/coupling, often just called a torque-converter, there is a third member, the stator, as shown in Figs. 5.9 and 5.10. When the oil is moving steadily, not accelerating, the sum of the torques on all three components has to balance out. So generally the torque on the output is not equal and opposite to that on the input alone; it can be more or less. In automotive designs it is made to be more. There is, of course, no way in which the output power could be made to exceed the input power, so when the torque is multiplied, the speed must be reduced; again there is slip.

In practice an automotive torque converter can develop an output torque up to two or two-and-a-half times its input torque. This happens when the output is stalled, vehicle stationary, and the engine is driven hard. When the vehicle begins to move, and the output speed starts to rise towards input speed, the torques begin to equalise. The stator is now unnecessary. So it is usually mounted on a one-way clutch, or freewheel. At low output speeds it is locked to the casing, and contributes to the output torque; the whole assembly acts as a torque converter. At higher speeds the stator spins idly in the oil flow; it is now inactive, and the whole assembly acts as a fluid coupling.

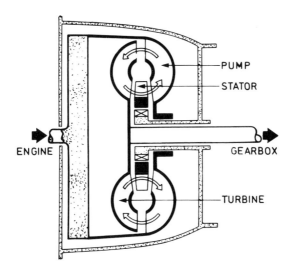

Fig. 5.9 Coupling/Converter (schematic)

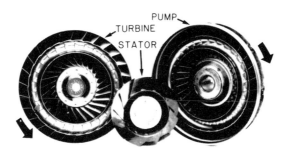

Fig. 5.10 Coupling/Converter (photo)

Thus a torque-converter provides both an automatic clutch at starting from rest
and a degree of "lowering" of the gear in use, automatically without changing gear.
In the latter capacity it is equivalent to perhaps one-and-a-half extra gears in
the gearbox. If adequately cooled, it can also allow for continuous low-speed movement. It is usually combined with an automatic-change epicyclic gearbox, perhaps
with manual over-ride, and the combination gives great ease of driving. On the
debit side, however, when slipping it does introduce considerable power loss into
the drive-line, additional to those mentioned earlier in epicyclic gearboxes. Not
only does the loss degrade the power actually available at the sprockets for propelling the vehicle, but it adds to the heat load from radiators, charge coolers,
etc. which has to be ejected from the hull. So the problem of achieving credibly
armoured top-decks in AFVs is aggravated. For these reasons, torque-converters
are often mechanically locked up solid when the vehicle is running in the higher
gears. This leaves them free to exercise their greatest value in low gear, when
starting from rest, particularly on steep upgrades, and when moving very slowly.

Hydrostatic Drives

In hydrokinetic drives, the power is transmitted by very large flows of oil, moving
with fairly small pressure changes. Alternatively, small amounts of oil can be
pumped through large pressure changes. The latter concept leads to hydrostatic
drive. The principle is shown in Fig. 5.11(a) and (b).

If the rotor in Fig. 5.11(a) is driven round about its fixed central support shaft,
the radial piston will move in and out, because the casing or stator is eccentric to
the rotor. From 9 o'clock to 3 o'clock it will move out, and from 3 to 9 back in.
As it moves out, the port at the top of the cylinder will be aligned with the inlet
port on the top of the support shaft, and with the delivery port on the underside
as it moves back in. So oil will be alternately sucked in and driven out. This is
a form of oil pump.

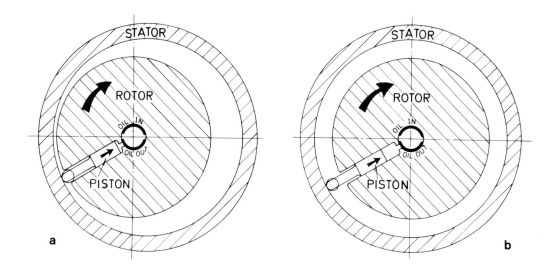

Fig. 5.11 Variable displacement pump principle

Suppose now that high-pressure oil be supplied to the delivery port. It will try to drive the piston out, and this can be accomplished only by the rotor's turning anti-clockwise. So the same mechanism can double as a hydraulic motor. Two of them, interconnected by a pair of oil pipes, can transmit power over a distance. If the oil pipes are made flexible, relative movement between the pump and the motor becomes possible, leading to the concept of a separate hydrostatic motor at each wheel station, all energised by one common engine driven pump.

Now suppose the pump casing be moved to the left, as shown in Fig. 5.11(b). When it becomes concentric with the rotor, the in/out motion of the piston ceases, and pumping stops. As it moves towards concentricity, the pumping is progressively reduced and, for a fixed pump rotational speed, the hydraulic motor will slow down. At constant input speed, this system can give continuously variable output speed. If the stator moves leftwards beyond concentricity, the motor output will reverse. This is exactly what we require for vehicular drive.

This looks like an ideal vehicle transmission system. Unfortunately, it cannot compete at present with mechanical systems in the matter of power loss. So its use is confined to a few special applications, including tracked vehicle steering, as we shall see. In practice, the system described would have not one but several radial pistons in the rotors of both pump and motor. There are also very many other layouts of pump and motor for achieving the same effect.

The use of an engine-driven generator to energise electric motors at the wheel stations is another solution to the transmission problem, capable, like hydrostatics, of steplessly varying the transmission ratio. But it too fails to compete with mechanical and hydrokinetic/mechanical systems on grounds of power loss, cost and bulk. It has found limited application, diesel/electric rail traction for example, and at least one wheeled AFV. But it seems unlikely to become usual.

UNIVERSAL AND CONSTANT VELOCITY JOINTS

Universal Joints

In general, the gearbox in a vehicle will be fairly rigidly mounted, while the wheel stations will be moving up and down on the suspension; additionally some or all of them may be required to steer. So the driveline has to accommodate changes of both relative position and relative angle between its two ends. In a mechanical system, this demands universal joints of some sort.

The Hookes joint is widely used. Usually, the input and output shafts terminate in two-pronged forks, disposed at right-angles to one another. Their open ends are bridged by a cruciform member, pivotted in the fork ends. Each fork can pivot in one plane about the centre member, and taken together, these movements, at right-angles to one another provide complete articulation in any plane. This

Fig. 5.12 Hookes joint

arrangement can transmit power with a large angular displacement between the two
shafts. But if the input is rotated steadily, the motion of the output will undergo
cyclic speed fluctuations, except when the two shafts are perfectly aligned.

To achieve steady rotation on the output, two Hookes joints may be used in series.
So long as the angles made by the intermediate shaft with the input and output are
equal, steady output will result. Such an arrangement can handle the problem of
a driven rear axle, or a driven wheel station jumping up and down on the suspension.
The deflection can be shared between the two joints. But if a driven wheel is
required to steer too, the resultant angular changes will tend to be concentrated
in the outboard joint. Then the angles are not equal, and the resultant speed variations in the driven, steered wheel may upset the handling of the vehicle.

Fig. 5.13 Double Hookes joint

Constant Velocity Joints

To overcome this problem, constant velocity joints may be used. Figure 5.14 illustrates a Tracta joint, which has been used in some wheeled AFVs. Although now
obsolescent, and superseded by superior modern designs of joint, it is the
easiest to understand.

As in the double Hookes joint, the input and output shafts terminate in forks. In
these, the two central members pivot; this gives articulation in one plane. But the
two central members themselves can pivot about one another, in the other plane
at right-angles. Effectively, this is a double Hookes joint, with the central shaft
greatly shortened. Thus the whole joint can fit into the hub of a steered, driven
wheel allowing the steering angle changes to be shared between its two halves.

Fig. 5.14 Tracta joint

In a Tracta joint, the driving torques are transmitted via rubbing, sliding surfaces, and this incurs wear problems. More modern joints, Rzeppa for example, replace this sliding action by the rolling of balls in grooves. This makes them more mechanically viable, and it is this development that is largely responsible for the general acceptance of modern front-wheel drive cars.

DIFFERENTIALS

When a wheeled vehicle makes a turn, the wheels on the inside of the bend have less far to go than those on the outside, because they are turning at a smaller radius. Rather less obviously, with conventional front-wheel steer, the rear wheels will travel less far than the front ones, because, to some extent, they "cut the corner". If the drive-line does not allow the wheels to turn at different speeds, stresses will build up in the system, called "wind-up". Ultimately, these will be relieved by slipping of one or more of the wheels on the ground. These stresses can be very damaging to the tyres and the drive-line, and the ultimate slip can cause handling problems. Differentials can prevent them.

Bevel differential

Figure 5.15 illustrates the most common of the differential mechanisms, though there are several other forms. The input drives a carrier, which carries bevel planet gears. These planets can rotate in the carrier, but in normal run they do not. They merely rotate with the carrier as though they were a solid part of it. So they force the bevel suns to rotate, and these in turn drive the output shafts, at equal speeds. But should circumstances demand unequal output speeds, this can be accommodated. For then the planets can spin in the carrier; this causes one sun to speed up and the other to slow by equal amounts. This bevel differential is the mechanism found in the drive axles of the majority of road vehicles. Figure 5.16 shows an example.

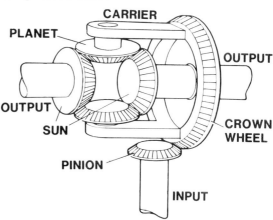

Fig. 5.15 Bevel differential (schematic)

Fig. 5.16 Bevel differential (photo)

Differential Lock

The provision of a differential between the drive wheels on the opposite sides of a wheeled road vehicle is very necessary, but it does introduce problems. Should tyre/ground adhesion be lost on one side of the vehicle, then there can be no torque

transmitted in the output to that side. But a characteristic of simple differentials
is that they transmit equal torques to both their outputs. So in this condition, no
torque is transmitted to the other side either. Though the vehicle may still have
good adhesion on one side, it can achieve no traction. In tracked vehicles, differentials often provide the basis of the steering system, as we shall see later, and
if the going be such as to encourage the vehicle not to run straight, the differential
will allow this. So tracked AFVs will often tend to "drift" down the camber of
roads, and require continual steering corrections to restrain them.

Sometimes differential locks may be built in. These may be directly under the control of the driver, or may operate automatically under high torque conditions, which
are likely to provoke wheelspin. Lock is usually achieved by locking one of the
outputs to the carrier. If that output is forced to turn at exactly carrier speed,
then the other one will do so too. For driver control, it is usual to provide a dog-
clutch on the outside of the main input gear to the carrier. When engaged, mechanically, electrically, pneumatically or hydraulically by the driver, it locks one output
to the carrier. For automatic lock-up, friction clutches are provided inside the
carrier, between the carrier itself and the back faces of the bevel sun gears. Under
high torques, the interaction of the gearteeth between the planets and the suns
tends to force the latter apart, and this action squeezes the clutch plates together,
locking up the differential.

All-wheel Drive

In cross-country wheeled vehicles drive by more than one axle is usual. But if
road use too is envisaged, differentials should certainly be incorporated on the
axles side-to-side. To inhibit on-road wind-up, the various driven axles should
also be allowed different speeds. This can be arranged by providing fore-and-
aft differentials between them, or by using one drive axle only when road-running,
and declutching the other(s). Figures 5.17 and 5.18 illustrates two such schemes

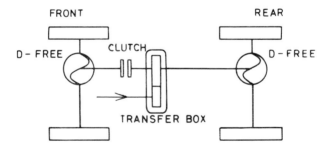

Fig. 5.17 4 × 4 layout

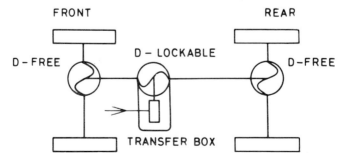

Fig. 5.18 4 × 4 layout

as applied to 4 × 4 vehicles. In the first, four-wheel drive is engaged only when LOW range is selected in the gearbox. In the other, selection of LOW range locks up the centre differential.

To maximise off-road agility, all the differentials should ideally have lock-up available; this is true for tracked vehicles too. But considerations of cost and complexity preclude the adoption of this optimum solution in the majority of real vehicles.

STEERING MECHANISMS FOR TRACK-LAYERS

There are four systems available for steering track-layers:

Auxiliary steering wheels, Track setting, Articulation of the vehicle hull and
   Skid steering.

In practice, many vehicles have incorporated more than one of these. For half-tracks, auxiliary steering wheels are the obvious choice. Track setting involves bending the tracks by steering some of the road wheels. It has been used on light vehicles, but needs back-up by some other system for making sharp turns. Articulation tends to be vulnerable and difficult to install in a fighting vehicle. This leaves skid steer, which implies adjustment of the track speed on one side of the vehicle relative to the other, as the commonest system in tracked AFVs.

Clutch-Brake Steering

The simplest mechanism for skid steer is clutch-brake (see Fig. 5.19). After the change ratio gearbox, the drive splits towards each sprocket, with a clutch and a brake included on each side. Disengagement of the left clutch would make the vehicle steer left. The sharpness of the turn would depend upon the severity of the going and the length/width (L/C) ratio of the vehicle; but usually it would be a gentle turn, and the left track would not stop moving forwards on the vehicle. This is a free turn. If the left brake is now applied hard, the left track stops and a relatively sharp skid or locked turn results. To make a turn of sharpness between these two, the brake might be applied partially, letting it slip. It would get hot,

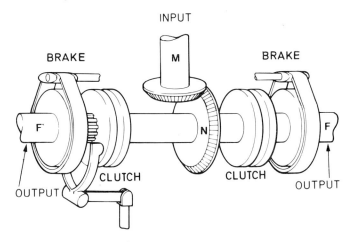

Fig. 5.19 Clutch-brake system

and this heat represents a waste of power. If systems can be devised wherein
there are no slipping brakes or clutches during turns, such waste will be avoided,
so the vehicle will maintain its road speed better while turning; furthermore, the
problem of ridding the hull of waste heat will be reduced. Such superior systems
are called regenerative; the clutch-brake system is non-regenerative.

With clutch-brake steering, a skid turn is the sharpest that can be made. But a
system that could cause one track to reverse, giving equal and opposite track speeds,
would make the vehicle slew about its own centre line, a pivot turn.

Clutch-brake provides a simple introduction to skid steering mechanisms and their
nomenclature. Indeed it is still used in conjunction with other mechanisms; but it
is crude. It provides little driver control over steer radii falling between those
of free turn and skid turn. Attempts to achieve such intermediate radii are non-
regenerative, and it can provide nothing sharper than a skid turn.

What is really wanted is a fully regenerative system, capable of a wide range of
steer radii. In general, a vehicle should be able to turn very sharply at low speeds,
to give good manoeuvrability. At the same time, there is not really much demand
for an ability to make controlled large radius turns at low speed; a series of shortly
held sharp turns will suffice. When running very fast, an attempted sharp turn
would probably be disastrous; at best the vehicle would slide laterally, out of control,
and it might well shed a track. A system providing sharp radius turns in low
forward gear and soft turns in high comes close to what is wanted.

Twin Epicyclic Differential

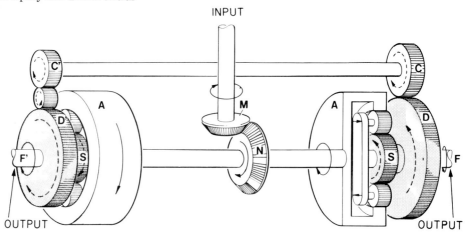

Fig. 5.20 Twin epicyclic differential

Figure 5.20 illustrates a twin epicyclic differential. This mechanism achieves the
same effects as the bevel differential in the drive-axle of a car. When the input is
driven, both of the annuli A must turn at the same speed. If the suns S are
stationary, then the planet carriers, and the outputs F and F' which are attached to
them, will turn at the same speed as one another.

Now suppose the suns were to turn as well. They are interlinked by the upper
cross-shaft, and on the left side only there is an odd idler gear between C' and
D'; so the suns must turn in opposite directions — though the tooth numbers are
such that their speeds will be arithmetically the same. Thus, the motion of one
sun will add to its annulus, while the other will subtract. As a result, one carrier,
and its associated output, is speeded up while the other is equally slowed.

So like the differential in a wheeled vehicle, this mechanism can allow its two output shafts to rotate at different speeds; and when this happens, its cross-shaft rotates. If then the cross-shaft is forced to turn, the outputs will have to rotate unequally, and as a result the vehicle will go into skid steer. On this mechanism are based the Merritt double and triple differential steering systems, by which the majority of current large AFVs steer, e.g. Chieftain, M-60 and Leopard 1.

Merritt Double Differential

Figure 5.21 shows again the twin epicyclic differential, but with additions. The cross-shaft linking C and C' passes solidly right through a group of gears and clutches. Input M drives through N', P and Q onto the annuli A as before, and if S and S' are stationary, the vehicle will run straight.

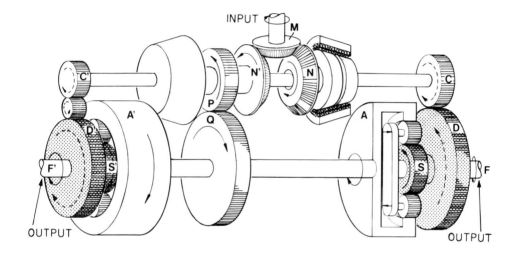

Fig. 5.21 Merritt double differential

But if one of the two clutches is engaged, the cross-shaft will be locked to either N or N', and these are turning, driven by M. Note that they turn in opposite directions to one another. So the cross-shaft can be driven at will in either direction. It then drives the suns and the vehicle is forced into steer, with choice of direction.

It remains to select how sharp the turn should be, without slipping any clutches or brakes, which would waste power. At any given engine speed on the input M, engagement of one of the steering clutches will give a fixed value of sun speed to S and S'. This creates a difference between the carrier or output speeds, and the ratio of this difference, one to the other, will depend upon how fast the annuli A are turning. If the annulus speed is high, the sun motion will have relatively little disturbing effect, and vice-versa.

Suppose P and Q to be just one of the pairs of change-speed gears in the gearbox. High gear will make Q, the vehicle and the annuli A run fast, so the suns will have little disturbing effect in steer, and the turn will be gentle; in low gear, the annulus speed will be low, and hence the turn sharp. As P and Q are changed from high forward gear to low, the ratio of the output speeds when turning increases, and this results in the turns becoming sharper.

This is the Merritt double differential steering system. The Merritt triple differential system achieves comparable results, and one or other of these two have served well in the majority of MBTs built since the early 40s. But now, new vehicles having significantly faster performances are beginning to appear, and these lead to a desire for still more steering finesse. It is now felt to be desirable to provide not only radius change with gear change, but superimposed on this, a limited range of continuously variable radius control in each forward gear.

Hydrostatic Steer

Generally this is achieved by a variant upon the double differential system, in which the cross-shaft is driven not mechanically by gears and clutches in a fixed relation to engine speed but by a combination of hydrostatic pump and motor, which can drive the cross-shaft in either direction over a limited range of speeds, continuously variable relative to engine speed. This is illustrated in Fig. 5.22.

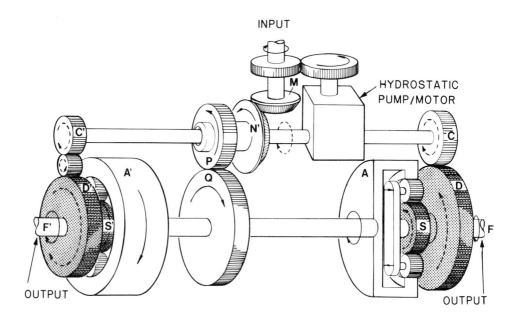

Fig. 5.22 Hydrostatic double differential

Most of the power is transmitted mechanically through the change speed gears and the annuli, so the relative inefficiency of the hydrostatics is not too serious. The pump/motor can lock the cross-shaft, as well as drive it, and this makes the vehicle intrinsically straight-running when steer is not required. If a brake is added to the annulus shaft, pivot steer can be ensured when steer is initiated in neutral gear.

Systems of this type are under development or in service in all the major tank-producing countries. They should permit near-wheeled-vehicle steering finesse in future fast track-layers.

CONCLUSION

Many Second World War tanks combined an aero engine or one or two large truck engines with a road vehicle change-speed gearbox. Then, by the addition of a few clutches or brakes, or of a very simple steering gearbox bolted onto the back, they achieved a viable power train, for the sort of performance then deemed adequate. Those days have passed.

In its own peculiar way, tank engine development has now progressed well in advance of commercial vehicle requirements, and modern steering gearboxes are complex integrated mechanisms found nowhere else. The power train now represents a large percentage, perhaps 15–20%, of the total vehicle development effort and cost.

SELF TEST QUESTIONS

QUESTION 1   With reference to the MBT of Appendix A (p.77), it is decided to make the gap between low and second gears small enough to ensure that the driver can engage low if the speed in second falls low enough to reduce the power available to 80% of the maximum. The engine has the piston engine characteristic of Fig. 4.4. What is the maximum road speed in second gear?

Answer   ....

....

....

....

QUESTION 2   If the same criterion is applied to all the gear gaps as in Question 1, what is the minimum number of gears acceptable?

Answer   ....

....

....

....

QUESTION 3   The MBT of Questions 1 and 2 is to be re-engined with a gas turbine. This new engine has the same maximum power of 1080 kW as the piston engine, and a power/speed characteristic as the gas turbine of Fig. 4.4. How many gears are needed now?

Answer   ....

....

....

....

QUESTION 4   The MBT of Questions 1 and 2 is to have its power increased by 50%, but the "shape" of its power/speed curve will be unchanged. Will this affect the number of gears needed, and if so, which way?

Answer   ....

....

....

QUESTION 5   Referring to Fig. 5.5, if the sun is driven clockwise and the carrier driven anti-clockwise, which way will the annulus go?

Answer   ....

....

QUESTION 6   Would it be possible to achieve overdrive with a simple epicyclic
              gear train?

              Answer   ....

                        ....

QUESTION 7   Three vehicles of the same weight have the same engines and gear-
              boxes. One is fitted with an ordinary friction clutch, the second
              has a centrifugal clutch and the third a torque converter. How do
              their hill-start abilities compare?

              Answer   ....

                        ....

                        ....

                        ....

QUESTION 8   Has clutch-brake steering any advantage over a double differential
              in road running?

              Answer   ....

                        ....

                        ....

QUESTION 9   Will a vehicle having Merritt double differential steering make a
              pivot turn under any conditions?

              Answer   ....

                        ....

                        ....

QUESTION 10   What possible peculiarity might arise in the steering behaviour of
              a vehicle having Merritt double differential steering when it is
              reversing?

              Answer   ....

                        ....

                        ....

Answers on page 222.

6. Running Gear

INTRODUCTION

If a vehicle is to make full use of the torque at the sprocket or wheel made available from the power train, a well-matched design of running gear is essential. The two main objectives of this running gear are optimisation of performance and of ride from which can be deduced the necessary component parts.

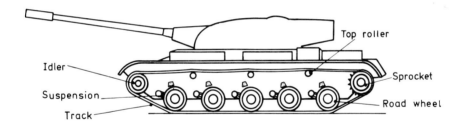

Fig. 6.1 Tracked vehicle running gear

Performance

Firstly the aim must be to make the best use of the available grip offered by the ground, in order to take full advantage of the drive torque, and so maximise tractive effort and vehicle performance. This will call for correct design of the ground/vehicle interface components; that is the tracks of a tracked vehicle, or the tyres in the case of a wheeled one.

Perhaps less obviously, it will also be necessary to ensure that this tractive effort is spread over the contact area as evenly as possible to avoid localised over-stressing of the soil in shear. To ensure this the weight of the vehicle must be evenly distributed over the ground, and this will call for a large number of road wheels. However, since the ground will in general be uneven, it will be necessary, if all these wheels are to carry their share of load, to interpose some form of suspension between the wheels and the hull.

Attention to maximising tractive effort is only half the story. The effort put into achieving this will largely be negated if an unnecessarily high proportion has to be expended in overcoming rolling resistance. On a hard surface, in the case of a tracked vehicle, much of rolling resistance is due to the track itself and is affected by those components designed to guide its path, namely the idler, sprocket and top rollers. On soft going the greater part of the rolling resistance stems from the inevitable sinkage, up to the limiting point when the resistance matches the traction and the vehicle is immobilised. To minimise sinkage we must spread the weight over as large an area as possible: this is a matter of track/wheel design. We must also aim to make the ground pressure distribution uniform, which reinforces the need previously put forward for a form of wheel suspension.

Ride

Increasing emphasis on the importance of both tactical mobility and battlefield agility, in the overall design of the modern AFV, has resulted in a call for ever higher on-road and cross-country speeds: this requirement has been met in part by the rise in vehicle power/weight ratios now considered to be necessary. However, the achievement of these speeds is to no purpose unless the payload, be it crew or equipment, arrives at the end of journey in a fit condition to fight: this will be dictated by the quality of the ride imparted.

Furthermore, in the case of the MBT, the ability to fire on the move is nowadays considered essential. This is achieved by the servo-stabilisation provided by increasingly sophisticated gun control gear. The performance possible is, however, limited by considerations of power and weight and it is necessary that the control task should be eased by the provision of a reasonably stable gun platform.

To meet these requirements it is necessary to try to isolate the hull from the accelerations due to ground irregularity and vehicle motion, and this is a further task that falls to the suspension system. In the case of the wheeled vehicle, the tyres also will have a role to play here.

We can now summarise the functional requirements of the AFV running gear as follows. It must support the vehicle weight with a low ground pressure: such support should be uniform and independent of the irregularity of the ground. It must attenuate the shock and vibration transmitted to the hull by that irregularity when moving at speed. Interaction with the ground should produce maximum traction, and finally all this should be achieved with minimum power loss within the system. Subsequent sections will look at each component part of the running gear in turn in order to see how these requirements can best be met.

TYRES FOR WHEELED VEHICLES

The wheel may be considered to be the most fundamental component of a land vehicle, and as such has been around for many millennia. It is only relatively recently, however, that the pneumatic tyre was devised to cushion the wheel against road shocks. Although the resulting improvement to ride is a useful attribute to the on-road mobility of the wheeled AFV, priority with this class of vehicle must be given to its ability to move cross-country, and in this context it is the off-road performance characteristics of the tyre which assume most importance. Thus here we are looking for low ground pressure and minimum soft ground rolling resistance, together with good traction. Furthermore, since we are talking about vehicles that will be exposed to enemy fire, the ability to withstand damage whilst maintaining some mobility is essential, if necessary at the expense of ride quality.

Tread Pattern

For use on paved surfaces the requirement is for as large a dry contact area as
possible between the tyre and road. The sole purpose of the pattern is to remove
water from under the tyre by a dual process of bulk displacement through large
grooves, followed by elimination of the remaining film by knife-cuts. Unfortunately
when it comes to off-road usage the need is for something rather different. To
understand the basis for cross-country tyre pattern designs it is necessary to
digress briefly to look at the nature of soils and the way they transmit traction.
The principles involved will be equally applicable to the design of track links.

Shear is transmitted between the surface of the ground and the bottom of the tyre/
track by what is essentially dry (coulomb) friction; this is true whatever the nature
of the soil. Within the soil, however, the transmission of shear is more complex,
being in general made up of two components. One part is due to the friction between
the soil particles and the other due to the "cohesion", whereby certain types of
soil contain fine elements that cling together when moist.

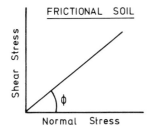
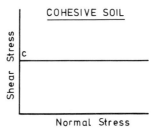

Fig. 6.2 Soil characteristics

A frictional soil is characterised by having a shear strength proportional to normal
stress (i.e. it follows the law of coulomb friction), and is devoid of any cohesion.
It is typified by dry sand and can transmit a tractive force equal to about 60% of
the load carried (ϕ = 33°). It is independent of the area of contact. Because
the friction between tyre and sand is greater than that between the sand particles
themselves, shear takes place within the sand itself and traction will thus be
unaffected by the tyre pattern. Indeed the effect of an aggressive tread is
detrimental, due to the disturbance it imposes upon the generally harder surface
layers of sand. Thus the need here is for a comparatively smooth tread. Additionally, although it will not help traction, a large contact area will aid mobility
by minimising sinkage and thus rolling resistance.

At the other end of the spectrum we have the purely cohesive soil where the shear
strength is independent of loading. This applies to all soil containing more than
20% clay, provided it is saturated, which is normally the case below the top few
millimetres of the surface. The large majority of soils met in Europe fall into this
category. The cohesion c is heavily dependent upon moisture content, ranging
from near zero on very wet clay to 150 kN/m² or more on stiff clay. Because
the shear force obtainable by friction between the tyre and the surface is
usually less in this type of soil than that obtainable by cohesion within the soil
itself, tyre treads are designed with a lug that will dig into the soil and stress
a layer below the surface. The traction obtained will then be dependent upon the
area of this layer.

The design of the lugs varies widely: some examples are shown in Fig. 6.3. In
general they must be a compromise between the necessity for aggressive penetration

     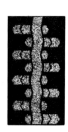

Fig. 6.3 Tyre tread patterns for cohesive soils

of the soil on the one hand and mechanical strength on the other. By adopting
a chevron pattern, with the direction of rotation such that the soil between the
lugs tends to be extruded outwards, a degree of self-cleaning is possible. Such
tyres have a poor road performance, especially in the wet, due to the small amount
of rubber on the road, and the absence of provision for water film elimination.
On-road they will also tend to generate structural vibration and noise, and have
poor lateral stability. If the vehicle is required to swim, aggressive lugs will
bring a considerable improvement in propulsion.

Carcass and Profile

For many years military wheeled vehicles ran on high inflation pressure (e.g. 700
kPa–100 lbf/in^2) commercial lorry tyres with modified patterns. The high ground
pressure of these tyres makes them liable to sinkage and hence high rolling resistance when used off-road. More recently ways have been found of effecting a very
considerable improvement by attention to the construction of the tyre carcass and
its shape. The approaches adopted have in common the aim of reducing the
inflation pressure and increasing the contact area.

At its simplest, the partial adoption by the military of radial ply, as opposed to
the stiff cross-ply, construction has been found to give considerable benefits in
soft going: this arises from the more uniform and lower ground pressure. For-
tunately, radial ply tyres are almost universal, commercially. Against this must
be reckoned the increased vulnerability of the thin side-walls to accidental damage
and penetration.

Use of a flexible carcass allows a very wide range of pressures to be used according
to the needs of the going. The Soviets especially have adopted this principle
widely: their vehicles are fitted with a central tyre inflation system feeding each
tyre through hub-mounted pneumatic slip-rings. The pressure range used varies
from 320 kPa on-road down to as little as 50 kPa in marshy terrain. The resultant
doubling of ground contact area nearly doubles the tractive force obtainable. By
lowering the operating speed with tyre pressure, tyre damage is avoided, although
some reduction in life has to be accepted.

Another way of lowering the ground pressure is to use a low aspect ratio (defined
as Section height/Section width). This trend has been noticeable for some time
amongst normal road vehicles for other reasons, but the use of low profile tyres
in off-road vehicles (as low as 50% or less in special cases) has been primarily
because of the large contact area made possible. The drawback with this approach
is that, for a given sinkage, the ground deformation (and thus rolling resistance)
is proportional to the tyre width. If an arched profile is used, then the active
width of the tyre will be regulated by the sinkage and thus not only will rolling

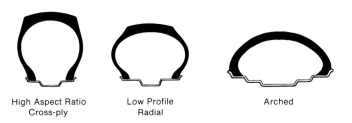

High Aspect Ratio   Low Profile   Arched
Cross-ply   Radial

Fig. 6.4 Cross-country tyre profiles

resistance be minimised, but also the available traction automatically adjusted according to need. Such tyres have found application in a number of military vehicles,
e.g. the lightweight Kraka of the FRG, but again it is in the USSR, with its large
unpaved distances, that they are most common. An inflation pressure range about
half that quoted for conventional profile tyres is used. Mobility is consequently
still further improved and there is an added bonus in the form of better tyre life.

Low Vulnerability and Run-flat

Considerable work has taken place in recent years to produce a tyre for the car
market that partly mitigates the disastrous effect on control of sudden loss of
tyre pressure at speed, and which then, as a secondary consideration, allows some
degree of mobility subsequently. In the application of the concept to the wheeled
AFV it is primarily the run-flat capability that is of importance.

Of the designs for cars, the most successful is based on the principle of a flexible-
walled low-profile, radial tyre on a narrow rim. Upon deflation the walls fold and
the wheel rim runs on the inside of the crown, with suitable lubrication. This
approach has been tried experimentally on AFVs, but has yet to be generally
adopted, principally because more development work is needed to extend the design
to large tyres and heavy vehicles, but also because of doubts concerning the ability
of the inherently less robust carcass to withstand the day-to-day knocks to be
expected with an off-road vehicle.

The opposite approach is to construct the tyre so stiffly that it is still capable of
carrying its load without undue distortion, even when fully deflated. This is the
basis of the British Army run-flat tyre which is in wide use at the present time.
Such a tyre works well but is heavy and gives a poor ride due to its stiff side-
walls. A variation to avoid this shortcoming is to use a rigid, or semi-rigid,
inner wheel of smaller diameter which only starts to carry the load when the tyre
collapses. This may be inside the tyre or else (in the form of a disc) bolted against
the outside when it provides a degree of ballistic protection. Only the latter has
progressed beyond the development stage.

A third approach is to compartmentalise the air so that, in the event of penetration,
only a small proportion is lost. This principle is used on a number of production
tyres for AFVs. For example, the French Hutchinson tyre is solid rubber, drilled
and the holes then pressurised. Cheaper and lighter is the use of a cellular foam
to fill the interior and this is the method most usually tried. Problems encountered
are the build-up of heat, which limits the speed, and the inability to alter the
pressure, which detracts from soft-ground performance.

TRACKS

Fundamentals

Until the advent of the self-propelled vehicle, the tractive limitations of the wheel on soft ground were of no concern. Its other shortcoming, namely sinkage, was apparently insufficient on its own to provide the impetus to devise a modification that would overcome this problem, perhaps because the ground pressure of the wheel was already no worse than that of the horse that pulled it. Thus it was not until the beginning of this century that the first practicable tracked vehicle was demonstrated, for agricultural use. The principle involved, of bridging the gaps between the wheel with a series of links joined to form a closed chain, was sufficiently developed by the First World War to make possible the birth of the tank, and continues unchanged in essence to the present day.

Compared with a wheeled vehicle of similar weight and size, the ground pressure of its tracked counterpart will be approximately one-third. The traction in cohesive soils, which is area dependent, will correspondingly improve by a factor of about three. Furthermore, in contrast to the complication associated with all-wheel drive, the track only has to be driven by a single sprocket.

There are penalties to be paid in return for these undoubted advantages. Foremost amongst them is the problem of steering. As discussed in the previous chapter, the normal method adopted, skid steering, leads to a complicated special transmission. However, more important, from the point of view of mobility, is the requirement for high longitudinal forces to be generated between the tracks and the ground to overcome the slewing resistance.

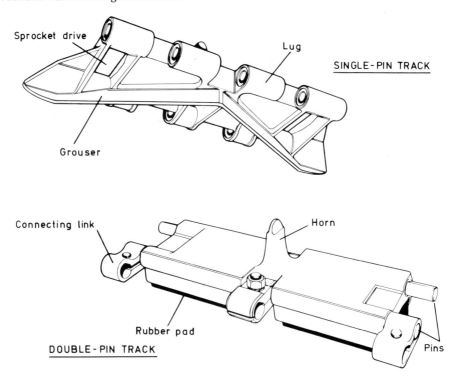

Fig. 6.5 Track link components

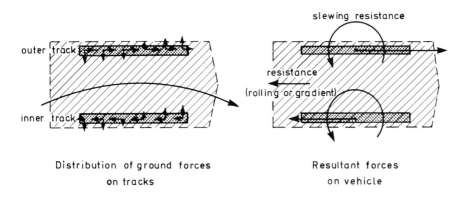

Fig. 6.6 Plan view showing forces during skid steer

The magnitude of these forces will, for a given weight of vehicle, be reduced by
placing the tracks farther apart (C), but be increased by lengthening the track on
the ground (L). Thus for ease of turning a low L/C ratio is needed; however, it
should be noted that this leads to wide tracks, more soil to be displaced, and associated high rolling resistance, whilst the short wheel-base results in pitching problems. For a typical MBT with a L/C ratio of about 1.7, as much as two-thirds of the
ultimate grip of the track has to be used to slew the vehicle: this is, perhaps, 100 kN
on average going. It leaves little spare traction to overcome rolling resistance or
gradients so that steering, under what might be thought of as only moderately
adverse conditions, becomes impossible. Under these circumstances, pulling the
steering lever merely induces track slip and sinkage, with the associated danger
of bogging down, whilst the vehicle continues on a straight path.

Single-pin Tracks

Figure 6.5 shows examples of the track pin configurations commonly used today.
In the case of the single-pin track, the lugs on the front of one link interlock with
those on the back of the next and are connected by a single pin. It is a relatively
light arrangement and, provided the number of lugs used is large, results in a
strong track that is resistant to stretch and enemy attack. At its simplest, the
pin turns in plain, unbushed holes in the lugs. It suffers the obvious drawback
of high wear rate and associated large friction losses. Wear not only limits the
life of the track, but necessitates frequent tension adjustment by the crew. The
hard manual labour involved can now be largely removed by the introduction of a
variety of hydraulic track tensioning devices. However, when the limit of adjustment by moving the idler has been reached, the crew are still faced with the task
of splitting the track to remove a link and then rejoining it. Bearing in mind that
a single tank track link may weigh 35 kg, and that a worn pin will be deeply grooved,
it is clear that here is considerable incentive to reduce wear if possible, quite apart
from other considerations of cost and logistics.

The alternative to the dry-pin track is to make use of rubber bushes, similar to
those universally used on modern car suspension links. Typically the rubber is
bonded between an inner steel tube with a hexagonal hole through its centre and
an outer tube which is then pressed into the body of the track link. The pin is
now of hexagonal section, so that all relative movement between the links has to
be accommodated by shearing the rubber as can be seen in Fig. 6.7.

With no rubbing components, the life of this part of the track is now limited by the

Fig 6.7 Rubber bushed single-pin link

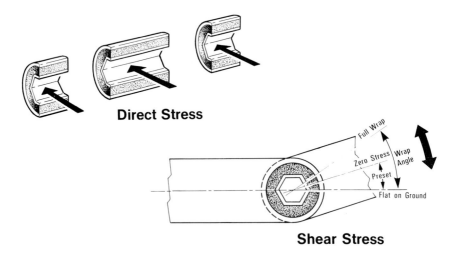

Fig. 6.8 Stresses in rubber bushes

life of the rubber. This is dependent upon the direct stress, caused by track
tension, and the shear stress which results from the rotation between the links.
The track tension which can be sustained, for a given permissible direct stress,
is limited by the length of the bushing which can be accommodated across a single-
pin track. This design is thus effectively precluded for heavy tanks, and it is
usually met only on the lighter classes of vehicles. The shear stress is minimised
by presetting adjacent links at an angle equal to half that required to wrap around
the idler/sprocket; when a new track is laid out on the ground, this preset
causes the ends to lift up, giving rise to the term "live track". Even so it is
desirable to further reduce the shear if possible. Both these considerations lead
to the idea of the two-pin link.

Double-pin Tracks

Referring again to Fig. 6.5, it can be seen that now each link carries two pins:
adjacent links are joined by separate connectors. The circular pins are bonded
directly to the bushes, as they no longer need to be withdrawn to break the track:
this is accomplished instead by removal of the connectors. Rotation of the pin within
the connector is prevented by machined flats. The length of bushing is now almost
doubled, whilst the rotation each bush makes will be halved, compared with the
single-pin track. With this configuration, therefore, rubber bushing becomes possible on the heaviest of tracked vehicles.

However, there are penalties. The extra rubber incorporated means that the track
becomes unduly elastic, resulting in a tendency to jump the sprocket teeth. To
get around this problem it may be necessary to run with a high tension, causing
undue loading on other components. The weight will be greater: this is an important
factor because tracks contribute 10% of the total weight of a tank. The manufacturing cost of double-pin tracks can be as much as twice that of single-pin tracks:
but this is offset by the much higher track mileage of around 8000 km.

Guidance and Drive

The high lateral forces generated during a skid turn imply a strong tendency for
tracked vehicles to shed their tracks. To prevent this, track links are provided
with a vertical horn that runs between the pairs of road-wheels and engages on
their inner surfaces. An alternative, utilising a pair of horns that run on either
side of a single road-wheel, is sometimes met on lighter vehicles.

Drive is transmitted from the sprocket to the track by means of sprocket teeth
that engage the links. Normally there will be a pair of sprocket rings for each
track, and thus each link is driven at two points. Reference to Fig. 6.5 shows that
in the case of a single-pin track drive is taken on a pair of suitably shaped holes
formed in the body of the link. The friction upon engagement and disengagement
with the sprocket teeth is high, and the associated wear on the link can be the
limiting factor in determining its life. On the other hand, the double-pin track
engages the sprocket teeth between its end connectors. Again the wear rate is
high, but in this case replacement is possible without scrapping the entire link.
With this design it becomes possible to replace the usual steel by aluminium alloy
for the body of the link, with an associated weight saving of 20%. Experiments
with this material for tank tracks are continuing.

Whilst the USA and FRG largely use rubber-bushed double-pin tracks and the UK
favours single dry-pin tracks, it is worth noting that the tank designers of the
USSR have succeeded, because of the relatively light weight of their vehicles, in
producing a rubber-bushed single-pin track. A further point of interest with this

track is that the drive is taken on the extremities of the links, where wear is less critical. This design also avoids holes which when packed with ice prevent engagement on the sprockets.

Ground Contact Surface

The principles upon which to base design for good traction were established earlier when looking at the pattern needed on tyres, and are equally applicable to track links. Thus for the majority of soils, which are cohesive, a sharp aggressive edge, or grouser, is needed: it will cut below the surface of the soil to utilise its shear strength. The tractive force will then be proportional to the area of soil being sheared, indicating the need for wide tracks and a large length of track on the ground. It will be noted that this is the same requirement as that for minimising ground pressure, and thus sinkage and consequent rolling resistance.

What then is the problem in adopting these principles? Firstly widening the track, as a means of increasing contact area, will push up the rolling resistance for a given sinkage, as a greater volume of soil has to be deformed. Furthermore, if the overall width of the vehicle is not to be increased, the width between the track centres will be reduced. When this is combined with the expedient of lengthening the track on the ground, the designer will soon find himself up against steering limitations due to excessive L/C ratio. Additionally, a wide track reduces usable hull width between the tracks and gives rise to high transverse bending stresses in the links.

However, perhaps the greatest limitation in practice arises due to the damage that an aggressive track will inflict on a normal paved surface. The extent of this is such as to be unacceptable to civil authorities in peacetime, with the result that all modern track links are fitted with rubber pads on their underside. It is significant that on a frictional soil, as will be recalled from the earlier discussion, this absence of aggression will not affect the traction. As training grounds are usually located on these relatively infertile lands, the adverse effect of pads on mobility will tend to be masked. The designer is left with two options. He can rely on lateral projections beyond the pads to give some grip, when the sinkage is deep enough to engage them, which is usually when the need for traction is greatest. Alternatively, instead of moulding rubber into the body of the link, he can make the pads detachable so that, in a period of emergency, it becomes possible, at the expense of some time and effort, to regain the advantage of an aggressive grouser. Furthermore, since the life of the pads is only about one-third of that for the rest of a modern rubber-bushed track, detachable pads that can be renewed bring with them the additional advantage of allowing the higher potential track mileages of these designs to be realised.

Attachment of the pads is most usually by bolts, but Fig. 6.9 shows an arrangement where retention is by a spring clip which is easily disengaged by driving a rod between the pad and body. To avoid the removal of all the 200 or so pads on a tank, it is recommended with this design that only one in six should be exchanged for the aggressive steel "pad" shown. A further noteworthy point is the addition of extensions to the end connectors, designed to increase the contact area with the ground.

TRACK GUIDANCE SYSTEM

Road Wheels

The fitting of tracks to a vehicle calls for a rather different design of road wheel,

Fig. 6.9 Double-pin link with removable pads

compared with its all-wheel counterpart. The need to engage a track horn has been mentioned, to provide positive lateral location. This results in modern AFVs all using a dual wheel design as shown in Fig. 6.10. From this also will be noted the other main difference is the absence of a pneumatic tyre. In the case of the tank, the reason for this stems principally from the role of the vehicle, which exposes it to fire more often than the lightly armoured wheeled AFVs. However, additionally it is found that the size of pneumatic tyre needed to carry the loads involved would be too great to fit into the space available. As a result solid rubber tyres are used. Even these present a design problem: as tanks get ever heavier and their road speeds increase, the tyres become liable to overheating.

To minimise tyre rolling resistance the need is for large diameter wheels. However, in order to optimise soft ground performance, uniform weight distribution is needed, calling for a large number of wheels. The normal compromise is 6 or 7 road wheels per side on tanks, whilst smaller, lighter AFVs use 4 or 5.

Top Rollers

The top run of track could simply be left to hang in a catenary between the idler and sprocket; indeed this is the practice on a number of tracked vehicles. One objection to this is that the arrangement will limit the travel available before the wheels hit the top run, with consequent adverse effect on the ride. Another

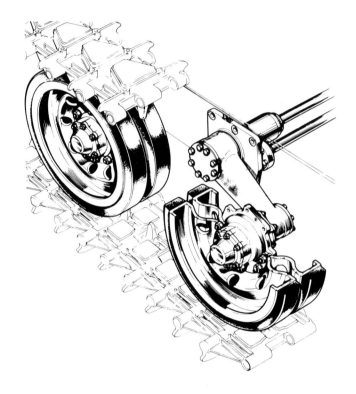

Fig. 6.10 Tracked vehicle dual road wheels

concerns the dynamics of the track itself, which results in lateral vibration reson-
ances taking the form of a travelling wave moving from front to rear (Fig. 6.11).
These may reach violent proportions, and the resultant fluctuations in tension can
cause an increase of as much as 20-30% in rolling resistance at certain critical speeds.

By making the road wheels sufficiently large, the top run can be allowed to rest
on the tops of the wheels. For reasons that are discussed later, the consequent
increase in unsprung mass makes this an unsatisfactory solution for the higher
speed vehicles, especially those with heavy tracks, and it will be found that modern
tanks all use separate top rollers to support the track clear of the wheels. A price
has to be paid for these in the form of added weight, inertia and friction.

Sprockets and Idlers

If large road wheels are employed of a diameter comparable with that normally used
for the sprocket and idler, then it is quite possible to replace either or both of these
by the wheels of the end stations without producing an undesirable increase in
flexure between links during wrap, and still maintaining an acceptable step-climbing
ability.

However, the complication associated with transmitting drive to a suspended wheel
has resulted in virtually all AFVs, either past or present, using a drive sprocket

12 km/h No wave in top run

68 km/h Wavefront reached 2nd wheel

Fig. 6.11 Track dynamics of Scorpion

fixed to the hull. The case with the idler is not so clear cut, and a number of
current tracked vehicles that utilise front sprocket drive make use of the rear
wheel in place of an idler, as shown in Fig. 6.12.

The decision as to whether to use front or rear sprocket drive will be based principally on the choice of engine location: there are no modern examples of drive being
transmitted the length of the vehicle. However, tests have shown that the rolling
resistance with a front sprocket can be as much as 50% higher than if a rear drive
is used. This arises because the full track tension has to be transmitted around
the rear idler, with consequential increase in friction losses at the pins and teeth.
Against this the tension in the top run will tend to inhibit track resonance,
and the additional length prior to engagement of the sprocket will allow better
clearance of mud and thus less chance of jumping the teeth.

Reference has been made to the use of the idler in the important task of adjusting
track tension. This is achieved by mounting the idler on a swinging arm which is
rotated manually, by a screw or hydraulically; in the latter case a neat solution

Fig. 6.12 Combat engineer tractor

is to use grease in the hydraulic cylinder, which can then be pressurised with a normal grease-gun. Such an arrangement will, however, only maintain the static tension. When moving over rough terrain, as the suspension allows the wheels to move up and down, the track tension will alter considerably. It may even become completely slack in front of the sprocket, with the accompanying danger of shedding. This is especially a problem with the increased wheel travel used in the modern AFV. To obviate this it is necessary to have dynamic tension adjustment and one solution, used by tanks in the USA, is to connect the swinging idler to the front wheel arm: such a solution is shown in Fig. 6.13. As the wheel rises, the slack is gathered in by the idler moving forward. The track tension acting on the idler will be transmitted to push the front wheel down, and thus this arrangement gives increased resistance of the vehicle to pitching, especially during braking.

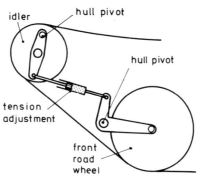

Fig. 6.13 Linkage for automatic
track tensioning

SUSPENSION

The Need

At the start of this chapter the purpose of interposing some form of suspension between the wheels and the hull was identified. It is to allow an even distribution of load on uneven ground and to minimise disturbance to the crew.

Let us look, for a moment, at a vehicle whose wheels are rigidly attached to the hull moving over rough terrain. By way of analogy, consider a stool that is set down on uneven ground; if it has two legs it will fall over, if it has three legs it will be stable with all legs carrying their share of the load, but if it has four legs then one will normally be off the ground. In the same way the vehicle will, in general, even when stationary, only be carried on three wheels, the remainder contributing nothing to providing traction or lowering ground pressure. Although sinkage on soft ground, or the use of low-pressure tyres which is in itself a form of suspension, may in practice allow further wheels sometimes to touch the ground, this will mitigate, but not solve, the problem. If now the vehicle moves at speed, the situation ceases to be static and contact may be reduced to two, one or even, at times, no points.

The effect on the hull of being supported at three points which follow every contour of the ground will be a complex motion made up of three components: vertical displacement (bounce), a rotation about the transverse axis (pitch), and rotation about the longitudinal axis (roll). In a military cross-country vehicle it is found that it is the first two that have the predominant effect on the crew and are used to describe the quality of "ride".

To gain some quantitative idea of the problem, consider a vehicle moving over undulating terrain which for simplicity will be taken as having sufficiently long wavelength λ in relation to the wheel base that bounce can be considered on its own – say λ = 10 m. At a speed v = 10 m/s (36 km/h) the frequency of the disturbance will be $f = v/\lambda = 1$ c/s and, assuming a quite moderate trough to crest height of 2 H = 25 cm, the corresponding maximum vertical acceleration can be calculated from the expression:

$$a = (2\pi f)^2 H = 4.9 \text{ m/s}^2 \text{ or } 0.5 \text{ g}.$$

The effect of this is that, even at those wheels which are in contact with the ground, the reaction will be halved as the vehicle passes the crests. At the same time the crew are being subjected to a level of vibration which, as will be seen later, can only be endured for a very short time without loss of performance.

Although enough has been said to show that a suspensionless vehicle cannot provide a satisfactory answer at speed, it should be remembered that the first tanks only moved at walking pace and hence the ride accelerations were negligible. That

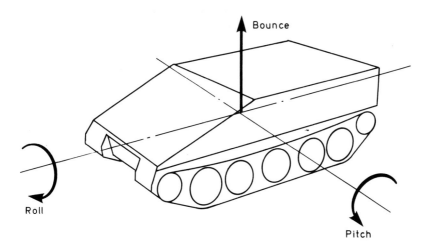

Fig. 6.14 Vehicle ride motion

left the problem of load distribution, and it was with a view to improving this aspect of the first generation of tanks that suspension designs were initially introduced. Since the principle involved will still be found on some tanks today, it is worth starting by taking a look at this class of suspension.

Bogey Suspension

If the weight of the vehicle is to be equally shared amongst the wheels, independent of the ground contour, then it becomes necessary to reduce the effective number of points of suspension from the hull to not more than three or, considering bounce and pitch only, two on each side. This can be done by placing pairs of wheels at either end of a pivoted beam, so that the load carried at the pivot must be shared equally between them, up to the limit of displacement. The principle is shown for a vehicle with four wheel stations in Fig. 6.15 from which it can also be seen how the idea can be extended to greater numbers of wheel stations. Although intended primarily to improve ground contact, the averaging effect of the bogey layout will also reduce the motion transmitted to the hull by short bumps: in the two examples, the vertical lift of the centre of mass of the hull is reduced to a half and a quarter respectively of what it would be with no suspension.

Nonetheless, it was not long before tank speeds had increased to the point where considerations of ride necessitated the introduction of some form of resilience into the suspension. In a variety of layouts this sprung bogey has been widely used in tracked vehicles up to the present day. In particular it has been favoured by British heavy tank designers in the form known as the Horstman suspension, which is shown in Fig. 6.16. An advantage is that, being a self-contained externally mounted unit, it can relatively easily be exchanged if damaged. Also, although this tends to be a heavy design, it is cheap to produce. One of the principal drawbacks is that it is difficult to accommodate the sort of wheel travel necessary for present-day speeds: for example, Chieftain has a bump-to-rebound travel of 240 mm, compared with 450 mm on Challenger. Another problem is that as speeds rise the inertia

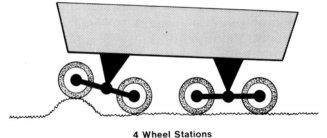

4 Wheel Stations

8 Wheel Stations

Fig. 6.15 Bogey suspension layouts

of the linkage within the bogey means
that the statical balance between the
wheels is upset and the loads are no
longer equalised as intended.

Thus, although the bogey suspension has given good service on
tanks with speeds up to 40 km/h,
the increased emphasis on mobility
has meant that all present designs are
based upon independently suspended
wheels. These will now be looked at
with a view to deciding what sort of
characteristics such a suspension
should have.

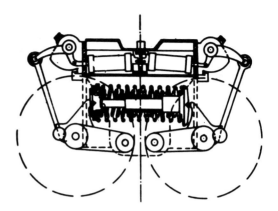

The Perfect Suspension

An ideal suspension characteristic might   Fig. 6.16 Chieftain tank bogey
be imagined as one which transmits no
acceleration to the hull, but provides a constant force, just sufficient to carry its
share of the weight, independent of wheel movement. The force/displacement
characteristics of such a zero rate suspension would appear as shown in Fig. 6.17.
Closer examination shows up a number of snags if this proposal were to be adopted.

The first of these arises due to the practical limitation on wheel travel. Because
of this the vehicle will not be able to travel at a constant altitude, but will need
to follow gradients and larger wavelength undulations. It is also likely to encounter
from time to time short bumps that are outside the range of the suspension. In
these cases the hull will have to be accelerated vertically, implying the need for
an extra force over and above that resisting the weight.

The next snag is the response to body forces. These are defined as inertial or
gravitational forces on the hull and will arise due to braking, accelerating, cornering
or change of static load. Because the zero rate suspension offers no pitch or roll
stiffness, a body force will deflect the hull up to the limit of suspension travel.
Again the implication is that an extra vertical force has to be provided under any
of these circumstances.

Finally there is the problem caused by fluctuation of ground contact. After a wheel
hits a bump at speed a large downward acceleration is required as it comes to the
top, in order to maintain contact with the ground. The force to produce this will
depend upon the "unsprung mass", which means that wheels should be kept as light
as possible. However, that provided by the zero rate suspension remains constant,
even when the wheel leaves the ground and flies upwards towards the hull. This
would result in the wheel frequently hitting the bump stop, with resultant shock,
and also would have a bad effect upon traction and steering. Once more a suspension that offers an increasing force, in response to a rising wheel, is indicated.

Passive Suspension

The most straightforward solution to the problem outlined above is to use a suspension
that provides a force that increases with deflection in a chosen and fixed manner.
Such a response is provided by any of the various forms of spring whose characteristics cannot be altered, i.e. which are "passive". Most commonly the force increases
linearly as the wheel moves from rebound, through static, to full bump as can be
seen in Fig. 6.17.

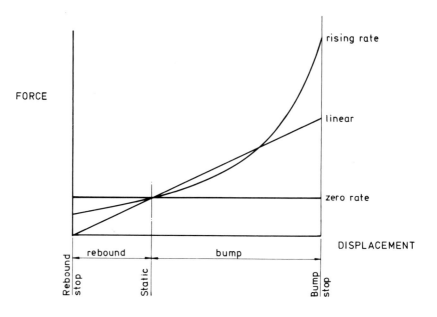

Fig. 6.17 Suspension characteristics

The cost of departing from the zero rate spring is, however, that now any wheel movement alters the force in the suspension, even when this is not needed, and thus produces an acceleration on the hull. The lower the suspension rate, the less will be this effect, but the greater will be the problems arising from limited wheel travel, body forces and unsprung mass. Thus designs using passive elements will always be a compromise between these conflicting interests.

A measure that mitigates the problem is to adopt a spring that offers a rising rate (see Fig. 6.17). To avoid hitting the bump stops too frequently it has been found that a force at full bump equal to about five times that at the static position is desirable in a high-speed off-road vehicle. With a linear rate this cannot be achieved without adopting an undesirably stiff spring and reduced rebound travel. Adoption of a rising rate is seen to allow a soft spring (represented by a small slope) around static, with a gradual transition to hard at bump. With this arrangement it is possible to have a spring with high energy storage potential (represented by the area under the curve) but a low stiffness for much of the time.

Although over the years many different types of springing media have been used on military vehicles, these have been reduced to three types on current tracked AFVs: torsion bar, coil and hydrogas. The choice amongst these is influenced by wider design considerations than just their effect on ride, and it is of interest to examine the characteristics of each with this in mind.

Torsion Bar

Here the wheel load is made to apply a torque to a circular section steel bar whose twist in response provides the required compliance. Since tracked vehicles universally locate their wheels on leading or trailing arms, it is convenient to use these as levers with the torsion bar running across the hull, splined to rotate with the

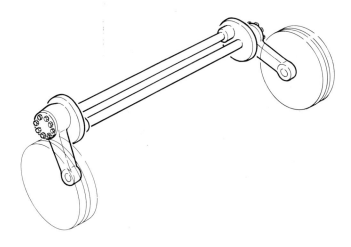

Fig. 6.18 Torsion bar layout

arm at one end, and to a fixed anchorage on the opposite side plate at the other.
The resulting layout is simple, light and relatively inexpensive. As a consequence,
the torsion bar has grown in popularity since its introduction on the German
Panther in the Second World War, until the present time when it is to be found on
all but a handful of tracked vehicles.

There are, however, a number of associated drawbacks, foremost amongst which
is the difficulty of obtaining sufficient travel. Properly designed, and for a given
stress limit, travel is proportional to bar length and this in turn is limited by the
hull width. With the steels available on early designs, bump movement was
confined to about 130 mm. To improve on this, double-length, hair-pin bars
were sometimes used. The principle has been pursued up to the present, but
avoiding the undesirable introduction of bending stress by replacing the return
bar by a torsion tube concentric with the first bar. Manufacture of the tube to
the necessary high standards of accuracy and finish presents formidable problems,
however, and the result is expensive. The other line to pursue, in the search for
increased wheel travel, relies on the fact that this travel is proportional to
$(stress)^{4/3}$. From the start special treatments have been specified in order to
increase the stress limit. Shot-peening the bar, for example, will introduce compressive stress into the surface, nearly doubling the fatigue life for a given stress
limit. Protection of the vulnerable surface, where stress is highest, by wrapping
or running the bar in a light oil-filled tube is desirable. However, the principal
factor that has allowed the torsion bar still to be used, despite the ever-increasing
stress demands, has been the continuous improvement in steel. Using electroslag
refined (ESR) steel the modern tank can now have a bump travel of as much as
385 mm using a single bar design.

The essentially linear spring characteristic of the torsion bar means that, for the
reasons previously discussed, it is difficult to obtain a sufficiently high force at
full-bump. This may be resolved by use of a well-designed bump-stop having sufficient resilience to act as a helper spring. A more gradual transition can be achieved
by introducing a second torsion bar acting in parallel with the main bar, but not
brought into play until the wheel arm has rotated through a certain part of its
bump movement. One application of this idea, tried in the USA, utilises a transverse torsion tube over half the hull width. A neat alternative, used by Vickers

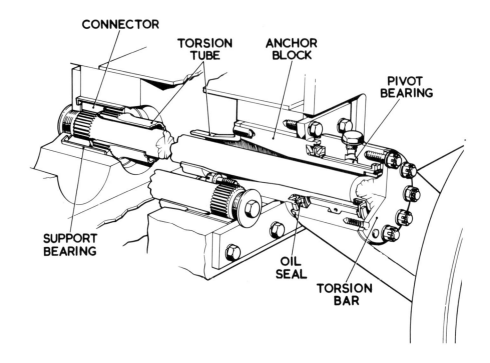

Fig. 6.19 Tube over bar suspension

in the UK, is to run the second bar within the hollow wheel arm, a simple pair of levers being used to transfer rotation of the arm into twist of the bar.

Another problem concerns ease of replacement. Although it is true that, being under armour, the bar is protected from direct attack, nonetheless the design has proved to be vulnerable to the hull distortions likely to arise from mine blast. Under these circumstances, it is usually the front bars that need replacing. As these are rather inaccessible, removal of the broken bar from its anchorage, into which it is quite probably corroded, can present considerable problems. An answer seen in the latest designs is firstly to strengthen the hull over the front bars, and then so to design the anchorage that bar removal can be performed from outside the hull.

A further important result of internal springing is that it becomes necessary to raise the hull height by some 100 mm, with associated consequences to the vehicle silhouette.

Coil Spring

Used in compression, a coil spring may be thought of as being a torsion bar wound into a helix. Although this disposes of the problem of length, the space in the centre makes it bulky and as a result the coil spring has normally been found on externally mounted suspension units. A good example is that of the bogey shown in Fig. 6.16. Here the central space is well-used by fitting three coil springs concentrically, the third being somewhat shorter than the other two so that its delayed action contributes to a desirably rising rate overall, despite the linear characteristics of the individual coils. The variation of stress between the inside and outside of the coils, together with the difficulty of treating all surfaces equally, means that the stress that can be employed in this configuration will be reduced by perhaps as much as 25% compared with the torsion bar. As a result it will be considerably heavier for a given resilience and has largely gone out of favour at present on tracked vehicles, although it finds continuing application on armoured fighting and logistic wheeled vehicles.

Hydrogas

The principle of using the compressibility of gas as a springing medium has long been applied in the air springs to be found on many commercial vehicles. These operate at low pressures of approximately 7 bar static and as a consequence are bulky, vulnerable and quite unsuited to AFV application. By operating at much higher pressure of about 100 bar static, the energy storage for a given unit mass becomes highly attractive, offering weight savings of perhaps 12 kN on an MBT as compared with a coil spring bogey design, whilst retaining the merit of being suited to installation outside the hull. The gas laws take care of the requirement for a rising rate, a bump-to-static force ratio of 5 being quite easily obtainable without compromising the desirable soft rate around the static position.

The pressure at bump, which would be 500 bar in this example, presents sealing problems if a piston in cylinder arrangement is used to compress the gas directly. An easier way would be to use a flexible diaphragm in place of the piston, but then it would be impossible to apply the wheel load uniformly to the diaphragm. The answer is to use a second actuator piston separated from the gas piston or diaphragm by a volume of oil, as shown in Fig. 6.20. Sealing is effectively confined to the actuator piston and since it is now oil that is being sealed the problem is considerably eased.

Adoption of this hydrogas spring, as opposed to a purely gas spring, carries with it a further number of significant bonuses. Foremost amongst these is that damping can easily be built into the design (this aspect will be discussed shortly). If the damper orifice can be closed completely by external control, then this will allow the suspension to be locked up, which is advantageous for consistent firing in the case of a gun vehicle, or earth-moving in the case of an engineer vehicle. The

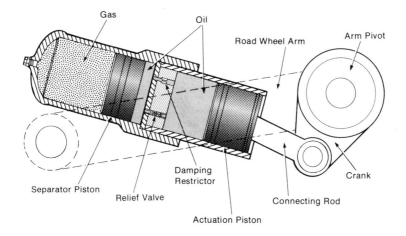

Fig. 6.20 Hydrogas suspension (Challenger)

addition of an external hydraulic supply piped to each suspension unit will allow the vehicle to be raised to provide additional ground clearance, or lowered to improve the silhouette. Perhaps of still greater advantage is to use the system to pitch the vehicle. This will give additional gun depression for firing from a reverse slope, the effect of which on the overall design has been discussed in an earlier chapter. In the extreme case of a fixed gun design, such as the Swedish "S" tank, this pitching can be used as the sole means of elevating the gun.

Disadvantages of hydrogas include the increased cost, perhaps half as much again, compared with rival designs. The variation of gas volume with temperature will lead to fluctuation of ride height which can be significant not only due to diurnal changes but also to heating over rough ground when oil temperatures can reach 130 °C or more. Maintenance will be more complicated with hydrogas, because special charging arrangements for the oil and nitrogen will be needed. Finding room for the cylinder between the road wheel and hull side can present a problem if it is to be made large enough to keep operating pressures within bounds. In this connection an interesting recent design proposal places the gas and oil cylinders one above the other within a monobloc which also acts as the wheel arm; rotation of the cylinder relative to a fixed crank then operates the piston via a connecting rod.

Fig. 6.21 "S" tank with hydrogas suspension

Resonance and Damping

Earlier the compromise inherent in adopting a finite rate suspension was discussed; it allowed the hull to be accelerated to follow the long wavelength (low excitation frequency) undulations whose amplitudes are outside the range of the wheel travel, at the expense of transmitting unnecessary force when travelling over relatively small, short wavelength (high excitation frequency) undulations. Unfortunately, when the dynamics of the situation are analysed, it is found that between these extremes there will exist a range of excitation frequencies over which the adoption of a spring will actually amplify the hull response to the ground input, in some cases to an alarming degree.

To see why this is so let us look, for simplicity, at the bounce motion alone, so that the vehicle may be taken as a mass suspended on a single spring as shown in Fig. 6.22. Now imagine this model being driven over terrain, the wavelength of which

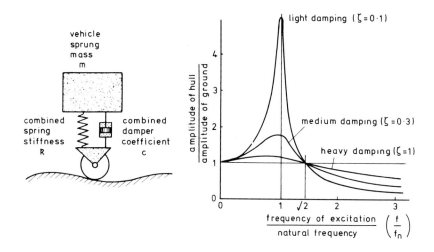

Fig. 6.22 Frequency response (displacement) of vehicle in bounce

is progressively reduced, so that the excitation frequency rises. The success, or otherwise, of the suspension will be measured by the ratio of the amplitudes of hull displacement to ground displacement. At low frequencies then this ratio is unity as the hull follows the terrain, whilst at high frequencies it drops towards zero as the hull remains inertial. Before this desirable state of affairs can be reached, however, there occurs a condition when the frequency of excitation coincides with the natural frequency in bounce of the vehicle, and resonance occurs between them. This natural frequency f_n is what would be observed were the vehicle to be pushed straight down and then released and allowed to oscillate. It is given by $f_n = \frac{1}{2\pi}\sqrt{\frac{k}{m}}$, a stiffer spring thus increasing f_n, whilst a heavier vehicle will decrease it. Figure 6.22 shows the behaviour just described plotted graphically, and two important conclusions are clearly indicated.

Firstly the introduction of a spring will only be of benefit when the frequency ratio exceeds $\sqrt{2}$ (i.e. when $f > \sqrt{2} f_n$); up to this point it merely serves to amplify the input. To reach this condition as soon as possible means that f_n should be kept low by the use of a soft spring and that the forward speed should be as high as practicable.

The second conclusion concerns the control of the resonant condition. The only way of limiting the resonant response is to introduce some form of energy dissipation into the system. A certain amount of this is inherent to any suspension, due to friction between rubbing parts. However, too much stiction is undesirable, as it locks up the suspension over small disturbances, and it becomes necessary to add a device whose sole purpose is to dissipate energy; this is called a damper. To avoid the problems of stiction it should provide a resisting force only whilst it is moving. If this force is directly proportional to velocity, the behaviour is termed viscous and is quantified by a damping coefficient c (lbf per ft/s or N per m/s). It can be approximated in practice by the pressure drop associated with the flow of a fluid through a restricting orifice. Unfortunately it can be seen that control of resonance by the introduction of damping is only achieved at the expense of increased amplitude ratios at higher frequencies, due to the additional force transmitted through the damper. Thus again, as with the spring, the choice of rating for a passive, that is a fixed characteristic, damper must be a compromise.

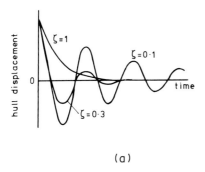

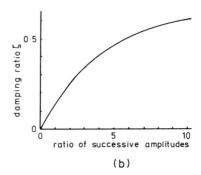

(a)   (b)

Fig. 6.23a Vehicle response following   Fig. 6.23b Relationship between
            a disturbance, for different   damping ratio and rate of
            levels of damping   decay of oscillation

The level of damping in any particular spring/mass system is measured by the
damping ratio $\zeta = c/2\sqrt{km}$. The amount by which different values of ζ will reduce
successive amplitudes following a disturbance is shown in Fig. 6.23. In practice
a damper that gives a reduction of not less than 3:1 is found to be necessary for
satisfactory ride, that is $\zeta \geqslant 0.35$.

The speed of early tanks was so slow that they operated well below resonance for
most conditions, and the inherent friction was perfectly adequate without the need
for any additional damping being apparent. As speeds increased and suspensions
were made softer, resonance became a problem and designers began gradually to
include a purpose-built damper into their units, specially at the end stations, where
they are most effective in controlling pitch. The problem of heat dissipation when
moving at speed over rough terrain has meant that AFVs have still usually tended
to be underdamped, and it is only the latest generation of high-speed vehicles that
have, of necessity, achieved satisfactory levels.

The telescopic type of damper commonly found on road vehicles has often been used
on military track-layers. Its performance, however, has been strictly limited,
especially in the case of heavy MBTs by the lack of a good heat conduction path:
cooling has principally been achieved by convection alone, as can be seen in Fig.
6.16. In the case of those of the latest designs of AFVs which utilise torsion
bars, the solution shown in Fig. 6.18 has been found by building a rotary damper
into the wheel arm bearing support unit. Because they are bolted directly on to
the side plates, which provide the necessary heat sink, these units can be rated
to levels not previously achieved. The mode of damping can be hydraulic, as in
Fig. 6.24, or may utilise suitably surfaced friction discs, as in the Leopard 2 MBT.
If the spring is by hydrogas then, as has been seen, a damping restricter is
easily included in the design, whilst again the complete unit may be bolted direct
to the side plate and heavy damping is thus possible.

Being velocity proportional, the force generated by these highly rated dampers at
present-day cross-country speeds can be very large and to avoid damage to them
it is necessary to fit a pressure-limiting relief valve. Under these conditions the
damper is acting as a buffer, usefully augmenting the spring and bump stop to
prevent the suspension reaching full bump.

Human Response to Vibration

Referring back to Fig. 6.22, when considering the frequency response of the vehicle,

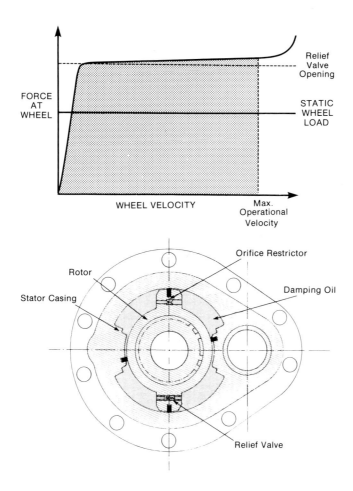

Fig. 6.24 Rotary damper on the British MCV 80

it was tacitly assumed that a sufficient criterion on which to judge ride quality
was the hull displacement. In practice this represents an over-simplification of
the situation: it is the effect of motion on the ability of the crew to perform their
tasks efficiently that is the final measure of the success of the suspension.

Figure 6.25a shows the results of tests in which the subjects were exposed to vibration of varying intensity and frequency, and their proficiency in the performance
of a set task monitored. It is seen that the human response to vibration (HRV)
is frequency as well as amplitude dependent. Man is most susceptible in the range
4-8 Hz, within which fall the natural frequencies of a number of principal parts
of the body including the abdomen, thorax, pelvis, heart, upper torso and shoulder
girdle. Consequently the acceleration of the hull should be minimised as far as
possible over this range.

The hull displacement response in Fig. 6.22 has therefore been replotted as an
acceleration response in Fig. 6.25b, and the general shape of the HRV curve superimposed. It can be seen that in order to minimise the overall effect of the disturbance on the crew, the HRV curve should be fitted in as low as possible whilst

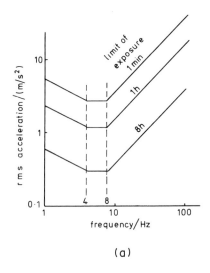

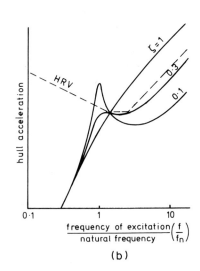

(a)   (b)

Fig. 6.25a ISO recommendations for   Fig. 6.25b Frequency response
effects of vibration on   (acceleration) of vehicle
fatigue decreased pro-   in bounce with FDP line
ficiency (FDP) in man

remaining above the curve of hull acceleration. Again the importance of choosing
the right amount of damping is apparent; too little results in high resonant acceleration, whilst too much transmits high-frequency forces. A damping ratio of around
0.3 is indicated; the best position for the HRV curve is then somewhere about as
shown, with the 4 Hz point coinciding with a frequency ratio of 1.6, indicating
a desirable maximum for f_n of about 2.5 Hz.

Active Suspension – the future

In this look at suspension design for military vehicles, the emphasis has been upon
the passive suspension, because it is the only type in production up until the
present. However, considerable work has taken place, and a number of research
vehicles have been built to investigate the possibilities of incorporating a suspension
whose characteristics, instead of remaining fixed under all circumstances, can be
altered to optimise the ride under the prevailing conditions. Such an "active"
suspension may provide an escape from the compromises seen to have been necessary
in choosing the spring and damper rates of a passive suspension. With conventional
suspensions approaching the limits of performance, further advances in this aspect
of mobility may be expected to rely increasingly on this approach.

In the block diagram in Fig. 6.26 the elements of an active suspension are indicated,
although not all the inputs shown will always be present. The suspension itself
will usually need a power supply which, for reasons of compactness, will normally
be hydraulic. Variation of the suspension characteristic can then be performed
by an electrical signal via an electrohydraulic servo-valve which controls the flow
of oil to and from the unit. The required control signal can be computed from any
of a number of pieces of information concerning the motion of the wheels, the hull
and even the terrain, derived from appropriate transducers.

Let us look again at the problems identified earlier when discussing the zero
rate suspension. Excessive deflection
due to load changes can be dealt with
by sensing the wheel-to-hull displacement, and using this to vary
the oil pressure in a hydrogas unit to
restore the full bump travel. This
can be achieved without recourse to a
computer; a mechanical linkage such
as that shown in Fig. 6.27a is sufficient. This form of self-levelling
suspension is comparatively slow
acting and would not generally be
termed active. If, however, the
response is speeded up, then the
principle can be extended to overcome
the problem of excessive pitch and
roll. Such a suspension would need
to be able to differentiate between
relative wheel movements due to
body forces in braking and cornering,
and those due to ground irregularity,

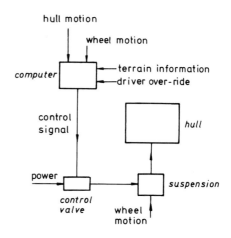

Fig. 6.26 Elements of an active
                suspension

and this could be done by monitoring the hull and wheel motions by accelerometers.
Again, however, it is possible to dispense with the computer and perform the task
hydromechanically, as shown in Fig. 6.27b. The system utilises a secondary mass/

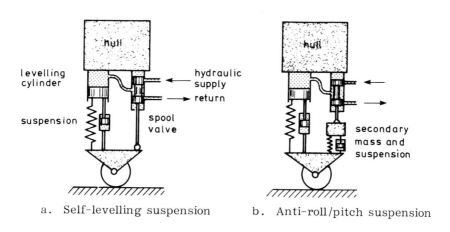

a. Self-levelling suspension   b. Anti-roll/pitch suspension

Fig. 6.27 Hydromechanical suspensions

suspension unit having the same dynamic characteristics as the vehicle mass/suspen-
sion and subjected to the same wheel inputs. A hydraulic supply is regulated by
the relative movement of the masses. The two masses thus move together in
response to ground irregularity and the valve remains inoperative; but only the
vehicle mass responds to body forces and then the valve regulates the pressure.
In this form the principle has been applied to two suspension research vehicles,
one wheeled and one tracked, designed by the United Kingdom Military Vehicle
Engineering Establishment (MVEE).

As a first stage in meeting the problem of limited wheel travel, provision can be made to utilise that available to the full, so that the approach of a large bump is anticipated by moving the front suspension to its bottom limit. This "preview" can be provided by the driver operating a pitch control. Finally, as speeds rise further, it will become necessary for the driver's function to be taken over by an inbuilt system of terrain preview, perhaps using a laser or radar scanner. Such a system would come close to offering the ride of a zero rate suspension by only increasing the force on the hull if an obstacle were sensed that was outside the range of the wheel travel. The problem associated with unsprung mass would also then be overcome without recourse to large additional suspension forces, by lifting the wheel in anticipation of the bump. Since the force required is inversely proportional to the square of the time taken to raise through a given height, increasing this time by a factor of perhaps five reduces the force by some 96%. Such systems have received considerable attention, but this has largely been confined to theoretical studies and they would be extremely expensive to develop and make reliable. However, they are perfectly feasible using modern technologies, and so may well be the basis of future suspensions should improved off-road mobility receive the priority necessary to justify the cost.

SELF TEST QUESTIONS

QUESTION 1   Describe a tyre tread suitable for use in:
             a.   Damp clay.
             b.   Sand.
             c.   Wet roads.

             Answer   a.   ....

                       b.   ....

                       c.   ....

QUESTION 2   Consider two vehicles of equal weights, one wheeled and the other
             tracked, on sandy soil. The sinkage, and thus rolling resistance,
             of the wheeled vehicle will be higher, but how will the tractive grips
             compare;

             Answer   ....

                       ....

                       ....

QUESTION 3   Explain the significance of the L/C ratio for a skid-steered
             vehicle.

             Answer   ....

                       ....

                       ....

                       ....

QUESTION 4   List four benefits deriving from the use of a double-pin, as opposed
             to a single-pin, track.

             Answer   a.   ....

                       b.   ....

                       c.   ....

                       d.   ....

QUESTION 5   What is the maximum speed at which a vehicle without suspension
             can travel over undulating terrain, having wavelength 15 m and
             trough-to-crest height of 40 cm, if it is not to leave the ground?

             Answer   ....

                       ....

                       ....

QUESTION 6   Sketch a three-wheel bogey suspension unit that will ensure equal
              sharing of the load between the wheels.

              Answer

QUESTION 7   Explain why, on a high-speed off-road vehicle that is sprung by
              torsion bars, it is highly desirable to incorporate some form of
              auxiliary spring.

              Answer   ....

                         ....

                         ....

                         ....

                         ....

QUESTION 8   A vehicle of mass 5 tonnes has springs giving a combined bounce
              stiffness of 300 kN/m. What is the maximum wavelength over which
              this suspension will attenuate the ground amplitude when moving
              at 12 m/s?

              Answer   ....

                         ....

                         ....

                         ....

                         ....

QUESTION 9   For the vehicle of Question 8, suggest a suitable value of combined
              damping coefficient.

              Answer   ....

                         ....

                         ....

QUESTION 10   A not untypical vehicle seat spring stiffness might be 60 N/mm. Comment on the suitability of this design from the viewpoint of HRV.

Answer   ....

....

....

....

....

....

Answers on page 224.

7. Protection

BACKGROUND

BACKGROUND

Man has always attempted to protect himself against his adversaries and the weapons being used, but this has always been balanced by his need to be mobile. Early body armour grew in weight with resultant loss of mobility until a weapon, the longbow, made protection, *per se*, a worthless asset and survivability lay in the reduction of weight and hence an increase in mobility.

A similar development cycle can be traced in the history of armour protection for fighting vehicles. Early First World War tanks were initially built of relatively soft boiler plate rivetted to an inner framework of angle iron. Increasing levels of protection in the 1939-45 war led eventually to the production of vehicles such as the British Churchill and the German Tiger tanks where the weight of protection provided put the design out of balance and made the vehicles slow and initially led to problems of unreliability.

The threats facing a modern tank on the battlefield are numerous. They range at the lower end of the scale from small arms fire, which although unlikely to injure the crew could well damage optical devices, to attack by other tanks and aircraft. In between these two extremes there is attack by cannon fire, locally bursting HE fire and infantry hand held anti-tank weapons. Belly attack by mines and top attack by aerially delivered weapons pose an increasing threat as munitions become more intelligent (see Fig. 7.4).

LEVELS OF PROTECTION

Protection can be split into three levels. The first is personal armour which is used increasingly in internal security situations but has no application to vehicle technology. Secondly, there is armour for light vehicles; at this level it is impossible to consider protection against all likely forms of attack, but it will normally be designed to contain attack by cannon fire or similar APC mounted weapons. Finally we have comprehensive armour protection; this entails maximum protection that the designer can provide to give protection over a wide arc against the major threat.

Early tanks had an equal level of protection all round the vehicle and this was necessary and sensible as they were subject to attack by a variety of weapons from all angles. At that time attack was non-specialised because there were no weapons developed specially to attack armoured vehicles. As weapons developed, so did the materials to protect against the attack, but it quickly became apparent that the sheer weight of the armour needed would make it impossible to provide all-round protection at the higher levels. Common sense dictated that the majority of the attacks would be directed towards the front of the vehicle which would normally be facing the enemy, so the preponderance of armour tended to be distributed over the frontal arc.

Whittaker's DPV

The first really serious attempt to analyse the probability of attack from any given direction was undertaken by Lt-Col Whittaker. His studies involved the theoretical attack by anti-tank guns against a single tank advancing against them. This gave rise to Whittaker's directional probability variation (DPV). These theoretical findings were confirmed by data obtained during the Second World War and the DPV still generally holds good, although modern analytical methods are more complex and precise.

Figure 7.1 is a diagrammatic representation of Whittaker's DPV in which it can be seen that a third of all attacks will be within the frontal 800 m (45°) arc and 45% of all attacks will be within the 1066 m (60°) arc. Thus, if protection is provided against the major specialised threat over the frontal 1066 m arc, then the tank will be protected against 45% of all theoretical attacks. The chance of attack decreases significantly outside this arc and to provide full protection would not be economical because of the weight penalty it would incur. The diagram shows Whittaker's DPV and an elliptical DPV which has been derived from Whittaker but is more regular in shape and so is more amenable to modern mathematical analytical treatments.

British tanks have followed the policy of providing protection against the major anti-tank weapon threat over the frontal 1066 m arc but with certain qualifications. It is accepted that the turret does not conform to the same DPV as although the hull will normally be pointed in the direction of the threat the turret may spend a significant amount of time traversed to one side searching for or engaging other targets. The other implication from this DPV is that it is better to reduce the size of the frontal arc which is given full protection rather than reduce the level of protection given. This then leads to the deduction that a reduction in size of the frontal area would lead to a dramatic decrease in the vulnerability to attack and hence an increase in the chance of the crew's survivability.

Structural Requirements

Any fighting vehicle must be inherently strong to carry such a payload as the crew and fighting equipment across country; the ground conditions impose considerable strains on the structure. The stress placed on the structure when a 50 tonne tank hits a bump at 30 mph is considerable, so there is a requirement for a strong basic structure. The stresses imposed by firing the main armament are also very large and as these have to be transmitted through the vehicle to the ground this also demands an inherently strong structure.

If conventional steel armour were used this would normally provide sufficient inherent structural strength, but even if an effective unconventional extremely lightweight armour could be produced there would be a limit to the amount of weight savings that could be made because of the structural requirement.

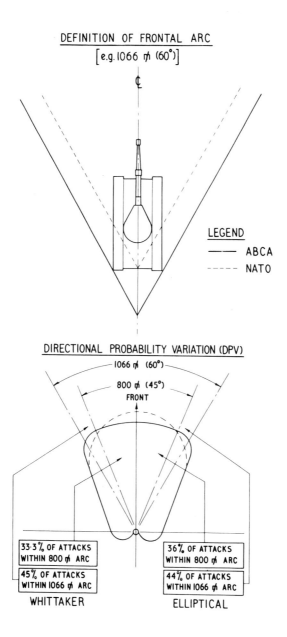

Fig. 7.1 Whittaker's directional probability variation (DPV)

ARMOUR MATERIALS

Rolled Homogeneous Steel

The classic material for vehicle armour is a range of special nickel/chrome alloy steels. Steel is a very versatile material and can be produced in a variety of forms, but most recent practice has favoured the use of homogeneous plate which has the same hardness and structure throughout. The production of the plate involves a rolling process to bring it to the correct thickness and to induce some desirable metallurgical properties. The armour produced by this method is known as rolled homogeneous steel (RHS) and is used as a standard of comparison for protection levels offered by other materials.

Thin Plates

For thin plates, up to approximately 25 mm, a fairly hard steel of approximately 350-400 Brinell is used. As this is not intended to provide protection against the major anti-tank weapons, there is some advantage in providing a face-hardened outer surface. This tends to shatter small projectiles and can provide added protection without an increase in weight. However, this material is notoriously difficult to fabricate and weld; consequently it can only be used in the simplest of structures. Another grave disadvantage is that if the plate is overmatched then the plate tends to fail catastrophically. If RHS plate is overmatched by KE attack the projectile will penetrate, bringing some debris in with it. The resultant damage will depend largely upon the remaining energy of the round. It is normally sufficient to put the vehicle out of action, particularly if we are considering the larger calibres. However, in lighter armoured vehicles it is quite possible for an overmatched KE projectile to pass right through a vehicle protected by RHS or aluminium armour.

Thick Plates

For rolled thick plates, over 25 mm thick, the steel used is normally in the 275-325 Brinell hardness range. Because of the nature of alloy steel special welding techniques have to be employed and electric arc welding is mandatory. A major problem is the distortion that occurs in the plate when large amounts of heat are put into the structure by the welding process. A very carefully controlled welding sequence is an essential. This is a complex and time-consuming process and hence an expensive business. The importance of the weld in retaining the integrity of the vehicle when it is under attack is paramount and therefore becomes essential that the welds between the major armour plates of the vehicle are fabricated under ideal conditions. This involves the use of manipulating rigs that can hold the structure at any angle so that the weld is always laid in the down hand position.

Cast armour

If a complex shape is required which cannot easily be fabricated from RHS then cast armour must be used. Until very recently this was almost universally used for turrets and very largely for the nose pieces. Although complex shapes can be cast with an infinite variety of thickness within the casting and infinite variety of curvature, it is more difficult to control the exact thickness. By the very nature of the casting process the protection offered for a given thickness is not as good as that offered by a similar thickness of RHS. A casting must be approximately 5% thicker than a RHS plate to offer the same protection, but this disadvantage is by far outweighed by the complexity of the shapes that can be produced.

ALUMINIUM ALLOY ARMOURS

Aluminium is now well established as an armour material, particularly for the range
of lighter armoured vehicles such as reconnaissance vehicles and mechanised combat
vehicles (MCVs). Although work on aluminium armour was started in the early
1940s, it was not until a need for airportable armoured vehicles was established
in the 50s that this work was pushed to a successful conclusion.

Aluminium in its pure state offers very few advantages and it needs to be alloyed
with other metals to give it the necessary properties desirable in an armour material.
It was found that by adding magnesium (Al/4.3/4% Mg) in work-hardened plate
the ballistic protections offered by plates of comparable areal density (kilograms
/metre² or lb/ft²) to steel plate was at least as good as that for steel against low-
level KE attack, but considerably better than steel against HE fragments. However, during the design and manufacture of the ubiquitous American M113 APC
the other advantages that this material had to offer were confirmed. By its very
nature and lower density the aluminium alloy plates are thicker and thus they give
the vehicle inherent stiffness which reduces the number of internal structural
members needed. The alloy is also much easier to machine and weld once the
specialist welding techniques have been mastered. Lighter components make
fabrication easier and all these factors combine to make production easier and help
keep costs down.

In the mid-60s Britain was contemplating the introduction of a new series of light
reconnaisance vehicles suitable for deployment by air, thus putting lightness top
of the list of design priorities. This naturally led to an examination of the poten-
tialities of aluminium alloy for the construction.

The Al/Mg alloy to specification AA 5083 used in the M113 series, although still
offering sound protection levels against HE shell fragments, did not meet the
ballistic protection requirements against 14.5-mm AP medium level attack. This
led to the development of a stronger, heat-treatable aluminium zinc-magnesium
alloy that also displayed good welding properties. This alloy to specification AA
7039 showed a marked ballistic protection advantage against AP attack over the
earlier AA 5083 type at all angles of attack. The weight savings in a comparison
against steel are also quite impressive: they vary between 6% to 20% depending
upon the particular angle of attack that is selected for the comparison.

OTHER ARMOUR MATERIALS

At one time it was thought that titanium alloys would become increasingly used as
armour material, as the ballistic protection offered by this material against small
calibre KE attack showed approximately 30% saving in weight compared to steel.
However, titanium is still a relatively rare metal; it is difficult to weld and fabricate
and it is approximately ten times the cost of steel. Expense alone would prevent
it being used on a wide scale in the construction of armoured vehicles, but it does
not show the significant improvement in protection against HEAT attack that would
be necessary to justify the greatly increased cost.

THE SLOPING OF ARMOUR PLATE

If it is the aim of the designer to produce a vehicle which encompasses the largest
interior volume for the least weight, then this could be linked directly to the
surface area of the vehicle. Theoretically a perfect sphere offers the largest

interior volume for the smallest exterior surface area. Although this is impracticable
for a vehicle, it is easy to see why a hemispherical turret is so attractive.

If we now look at Fig. 7.2, the armour facing the most likely angle of attack is
placed vertically so that the projectile would strike it at the normal, then the thickness it would need to penetrate can be represented by T_N. If the plate is then
sloped at an angle of β and reduced in thickness so that the horizontal thickness
remains the same, then the weight remains the same but the surface area of the
plate is greater because l is now greater than h (see Fig. 7.2).

Equivalent Thickness

The saving in weight does not stem from the simple sloping but from the consequences that arise. If we imagine that the plates in Fig. 7.2 represent those in
front of a driver's compartment, the sloping saves weight because there is a reduction in top and side armour. To give a measure of comparison, the thickness of
armour is normally expressed as EQUIVALENT THICKNESS, which is the length
of path a projectile would need to travel to penetrate if it struck the target

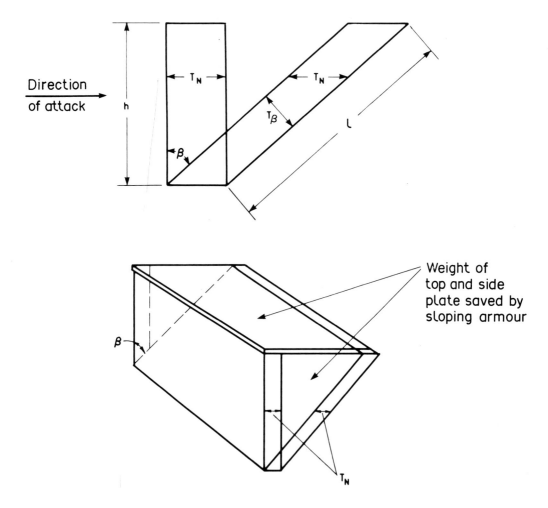

Fig. 7.2 Equivalent thickness

horizontally and at 0° azimuth angle of attack. Referring to Fig. 7.2, the actual
thickness of the armour material can be established by the formulae

$$T_\beta = T_N \cos \beta.$$

Because cos 60° = 0.5, it is easy to realise that armour plate sloped at 60° has an
equivalent thickness of twice its actual thickness.

Effect of the Vehicle Attitude

It is extremely unlikely that a projectile will arrive at the target exactly head on,
and although KE shot may be regarded for all intents and purposes to be travelling
horizontally, it is quite likely that the target will be inclined on a slope at the
moment of impact. Thus the angle of attack will be a compound angle of the actual
slope of armour relative to the vertical at the moment of strike (see Fig. 7.3).

If the armour is sloped β from the vertical and the projectile strikes at an azimuth
angle α, then the compound angle C can be found from the expression

$$\cos C = \cos \alpha \cos \beta.$$

Differing National Notations

It should be noted that the angle of slope is the angle from the vertical because
armour was originally placed at the vertical. It is important to establish what
is the basis for describing the slope of the armour because some nations describe it as the inclination from the horizontal. This can be misleading and the
cosine law for equivalent thickness cannot be applied directly.

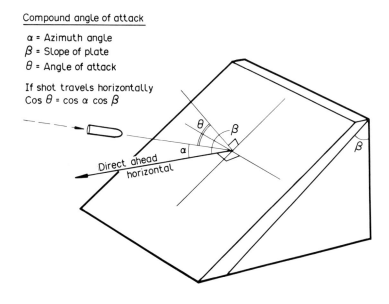

Fig. 7.3 Compound angle of attack

Additional Effects of Sloping

Some of the weight savings achieved by sloping the armour have already been mentioned, but there are other equally important effects. The mechanism whereby
a solid KE projectile, be it APDS or a long rod penetrator, defeats sloped armour
is a complex matter, but in neither case is the path taken by the projectile a con-
tinuation of its line of flight and the path length through the armour is discernibly
longer. Thus the projectile is forced to give up more energy to the armour material
than it would do if it continued on a straight line through the armour and the protection offered by sloped plate is always slightly greater than suggested by the
cosine law.

More importantly, once armour is sloped in excess of 60° there is a good chance
of inducing a ricochet. The exact angle at which ricochet occurs depends on a
wide variety of factors, but the design and nature of the projectile is the most
important.

THE IDEAL MATERIAL

Requirements

If we are looking for an ideal armour material there would be several factors to
consider; but the major consideration would be that the armour should be effective.
It must do the job it is designed to do, and it should be light, which in turn gives
a variety of advantageous secondary effects. Above all the armour must be cost
effective. There is little point in producing some exotic material which is so
expensive that it would make the vehicle prohibitively expensive. Other considerations are that the armour should be amenable to modern construction techniques and be readily weldable and be capable of being produced in a variety of
shapes. Bulk is an important factor because if the armour is bulky even though
its areal density is low it will be difficult to provide sufficient room under the
armour to meet the volume requirements for the crew, gun, ammunition, fuel and
power train, etc.

The Steel Solution

For many years various alloy steels have measured up to this requirement very
well. It is a tough material that is well understood and can be made with various
properties by changing the proportion and presence of the alloying elements. It
is readily available, the technique of fabrication into vehicles is a practised art
and it is also relatively inexpensive. Although it is heavy material with a large
areal density it does offer very good levels of protection against KE and HESH,
but its performance against HEAT attack is considerably reduced.

Most alloy steels contain some or all of the elements manganese, nickel, chrome,
molybdenum and vanadium to give a correct blend of high strength and resistance
to fracture or roughness.

The specific composition of the steel and the heat treatment afforded to it will
depend not only upon whether it is to be rolled plate or a casting. Most armour
steels are manufactured to specifications in the IT series. Thus IT 80 is the
specification for rolled steel plate and IT 90 refers to cast armour.

BODY ARMOUR TECHNIQUES

The Need

It is arguable that the earliest form of armour was not to protect any form of transportation but to protect the person. From mediaeval times the foot soldier was
protected with some kind of body vest, a helmet and a shield. When the scale of
attack was dramatically increased with the advent of firearms, any form of protection was easily overmatched and it was soon abandoned in favour of the greater
mobility given to the individual.

Some attempts were made during the Second World War to give some protection to
individuals who, although exposed, were relatively inactive and could thus accept
the imposed weight and reduced mobility. This application was found particularly
suitable for aircraft crews and the US Air Force bomber crews used "flak"
jackets to good effect. We have seen the popularity of this concept of body protection grow with extensive use by American troops in Vietnam, Israeli troops and
in British IS operations, particularly in Northern Ireland.

Candidate Materials

Where the total weight to be carried is critical, the essential criterion must be a
low areal density. Some protection against low-velocity small arms fire and shell
splinters can be obtained from suits manufactured with interleaved steel plates.
As soon as the required protection level is raised, the increased weight causes
unacceptable loss of mobility. 2.5 mm special steel plates will normally stop most
hand guns and a body jacket typically weighs 5-6 kg. Any attempt to provide
protection against rifle fire by the use of special steel plates would entail an
unacceptably greater increase in weight, with no assurance of total immunity. A
problem with all body armour is that if the energy from the projectile is not to
be transferred from armour to the body then a way has to be found to dissipate
the energy before this happens or the secondary effect may be equally fatal.

Ceramics are another group of materials that have been extensively used for body
armour protection and they are particularly interesting to the vehicle designer
as they show most promise as armour protection for light vehicles. The normal
definition of ceramics is the art of pottery, but in this application we are considering the manufacture of special materials into tiles which are extremely hard.
There are several candidate materials, but the most common are boron carbide,
silicon carbide and alumina.

By and large the ceramic layer must exceed the hardness of the shot. AP bullet
design favours high-density, high-hardness core materials such as tungsten carbide, so in order to shatter bullets made of this material the candidate armour
material must exceed this hardness (e.g. alumina or boron carbide).

All ceramic armours are extremely hard, but they are also brittle. They provide
protection because extreme hardness causes the projectile to shatter as the ceramic
tile itself shatters. Inevitably such armours can only offer one-shot protection
and if continuous protection is required then the tiles must be capable of being
easily replaced and this in itself is a drawback to their use in most applications.
The size of the tile is also important. If the tile is made too large, then when it
is hit and shattered it leaves a large unprotected area. If the tile is made small,
then although the area affected by each shot is reduced, the number of joins
between each tile is increased and must offer a lesser degree of protection. Smaller
tiles increase the difficulty of securing them in place, but if they are small enough
they give some possibility of providing more complex shaping of the armour than

Material	Hardness (Knoop)	Melting point °C	Density g cm^{-3}
Diamond*	7000		
Boron carbide (B_4C)	2750	2460	2.52
Titanium boride ($Ti B_2$)	2720	2980	4.52
Silicon carbide (Si C)	2480	2720	3.22
Titanium carbide (Ti C)	2470	3160	4.94
Zirconium carbide (Zr C)	2100	3030	6.44
Alumina ($Al_2 O_3$)	2100	2015	3.96
Tantalum carbide (Ta C)	2000	3880	14.5
Tungsten carbide (W_2C)	1880	2730	17.34
Steel *	900		
Quartz *	820		
Glass (soda) *	530		

* Included for comparison

is possible with the larger individual tiles. Apart from these considerations there are also manufacturing problems to be overcome if large size tiles are required. Common sizes encountered are square tiles of 100 mm and smaller octagonal tiles approximately 20 mm across the diagonal. Although ceramic armours offer good levels of protection for very low areal densities, they are very expensive to produce and are currently ineffective against large calibre attack. We thus find ceramics are largely employed for the protection of helicopters where weight saving is paramount. Their use in future as one element in a composite armour matrix cannot be discounted, and although they could be readily adapted for use as applique kits for the protection of unarmoured light vehicles their use in this particular application can currently be discounted on financial/cost grounds.

Composite Armour

It is apparent from the matters already discussed that if the form of attack can be predetermined then it is relatively easy to select the most suitable armour from all the candidate materials. If, however, the form of attack is not known and there is a distinct possibility of attack by several methods, then the choice of a suitable armour becomes a more complex problem. If each individual optimum protection method were to be incorporated into the design regardless, then the combination would give better all round performance but the penalty would be an excessively bulky and heavy armour protection leading to a completely impracticable vehicle.

Recent advances in material technology and a better understanding of their capabilities against attack has led to the development of the modern "Chobham" type of armour. Published information indicates that this type of armour can offer a greatly enhanced protection against hollow charge and HESH attack without degradation of the protection offered to conventional KE attack.

There is inevitably a penalty to pay, and apart from the increased cost and complexity of manufacture this type of armour is very bulky.. Thus, it cannot easily

be used to enhance the protection of existing vehicles but must be incorporated
in the design of a vehicle from its inception. An additional factor is that it is not
amenable to being formed into complex shapes and hence the slab-sided turrets
seen on the Challenger, Gen Abrams and Leopard 2 main battle tanks.

It has now become an essential element in modern tank design and it will be interesting to see in what form the Russian version will be manifested. Further progress
may allow the bulk to be reduced without loss in protection or, alternatively, more
protection could be provided for the same bulk and weight.

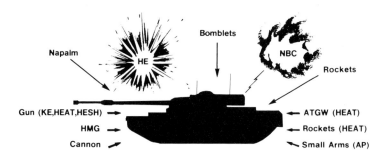

Fig. 7.4 The threat

SELF TEST QUESTIONS

QUESTION 1   What was the material used to protect the First World War tanks and how was it secured?

                 Answer   ....

                                ....

QUESTION 2   What did Whittaker's DPV attempt to analyse?

                 Answer   ....

                                ....

QUESTION 3   What are the disadvantages of thin plates when used as a method of protection?

                 Answer   ....

                                ....

QUESTION 4   What are the advantages of aluminium alloy armours?

                 Answer   ....

                                ....

QUESTION 5   What is equivalent thickness and what formulae is used to express it?

                 Answer   ....

                                ....

QUESTION 6   What are characteristics of the ideal armour material?

                 Answer   ....

                                ....

                                ....

QUESTION 7   What alloying elements would you expect to find in armour steel?

                 Answer   ....

                                ....

                                ....

QUESTION 8   What are the major problems with body armour?

                 Answer   ....

                                ....

QUESTION 9   What are the three most common ceramics used as armour material?

Answer   ....

....

QUESTION 10   What advantages are offered by composite armour?

Answer   ....

....

Answers on page 225.

8. Configurations

Problems in Defining the Requirement

Many armoured vehicles in the past have failed to live up to their expectations because the crews have not been able to operate them to their theoretical maximum level of efficiency. There are many reasons for this and in the early days this was mainly due to a communication failure between the user and the designer. Most countries now operate a sophisticated military "Staff Requirement" system which is intended to translate the military requirement into a clear statement which the designer can understand. With the best will in the world, matters may still go awry as the tactical picture may have changed since the requirement was initially ' stated and thus the vehicle may be called upon to fulfil a role which was never envisaged during its inception.

In the age of expanding technology, as new capabilities arise so quickly, it is often difficult for the soldier to visualise the application of a particular aspect to the tactics of the battlefield. In many cases it is just not possible to define the way the equipment will be used until some hardware is produced and is put into the hands of the soldier so that he can test the practical applications.

The Command Function

There are several aspects to be considered, but the most important are that the whole layout of the vehicle must be governed by its intended tactical role and that the commander of the vehicle must be able to exercise his command function. This is important for the commander of any armoured fighting vehicle, but it becomes a vital factor if the vehicle commander is also the troop or platoon commander.

The Scope of Crew Tasks

Additionally, there will be a number of minor tasks which have to be completed to maintain the vehicle at maximum efficiency. These tasks can normally be shared amongst the crew, but will probably not significantly diminish in magnitude or number if the crew size is reduced, and thus it is apparent that a reduction

in crew numbers can often mean an increasing burden on the remaining crew
members.

Apart form the prime task of manoeuvring the vehicle on the battlefield and firing
the main armament, the other tasks to be undertaken in action are loading and
maintaining any machine guns or other armaments, operating the radio sets, reposi-
tioning main armament ammunition to maintain a state of readiness, cleaning and
maintaining vision devices and running adjustments and servicing ancillary equipments such as the NBC filter equipment.

With the improvement of night viewing devices the ability of armoured vehicles to
fight a battlefield day of 24 hours has increased, with a consequent increase in
crew duties. This could mean a reduction in the time available for the crew to
undertake all those other tasks usually performed during a lull in the battle or
when the vehicle was withdrawn from the battlefield during the hours of darkness.
They include replenishment of ammunition, fuel, food and water; then there is the
cleaning and maintenance of the main armament and other arms; the turret and
automotive system require servicing, as does the suspension; the tracks require
servicing and old wheels need changing; finally, at every halt of over a few
minutes camouflage must be erected or changed and then possibly taken apart
before the next move.

In addition to these chores the crew will need to rest and eat. It is normal for
vehicle crews to be self-contained in respect to their feeding arrangements, as
it gives a greater flexibility, but it does impose an extra load on the crew. As
any woman will tell you, the last thing she wants to do at the end of an exhausting
day is to cook a nourishing meal! The effect of all this is an increasing demand
for a reduction in the number of crew tasks that need to be completed to maintain
the vehicle's battle efficiency so that the crew themselves can remain more efficient.
Obviously this involves constant consultation between the user and the designer
at all stages of development. It is often easy to see how modern engineering
techniques can reduce some of these chores, but it is normally at the expense of
increased complexity and cost.

Reducing Crew Duties

An automatic track tensioner, as described in Chapter 6, is such an example. In
modern engineering terms it is comparatively simple to design and manufacture,
but it is yet another complex component which adds to the cost and can also add
to the weight of the vehicle. Inevitably it is a question of trade-offs, and a compromise would probably be reached with a tensioning device that was not fully automatic but could be used to give some assistance to the crew in their tasks. This
would reduce the complexity and cost and at the same time go some way towards
reducing the crew load.

CREW NUMBERS

After the First World War and for a greater part of the Second World War, it was
thought that a five-man crew was essential for the efficient manning of a tank.
Sometimes the numbers needed were dictated by the armament carried.

The United States M3AL General Lee tank was an American medium tank under
development in 1940 when it became apparent that there was an immediate need
for a very large number of tanks. The General Lee was put into instant production
and very soon was put into action in North Africa. It had a slightly unusual configuration because the main armament was a 75-mm gun carried in a sponson on

the front right side, with limited traverse. The upper turret, which had all-round traverse, contained a 37-mm gun. This arrangement required a crew of six to man it efficiently and with its 75-mm gun it played an important part in defeating the German armour at the Battle of Gazala. Although a match for the German Pz Kp 3, particularly at short ranges, it suffered from the grave disadvantage that it had to expose a large part of its hull in order to engage the enemy.

Most nations favoured the five-man crew, as they believed that the extra member was essential as a co-driver. Certainly, the tanks of those days were not simple vehicles to drive and required considerable physical effort. If a long approach march were to be undertaken or indeed if the driver was required to be in the seat for any length of time, then a co-driver became essential. In addition to his standby driving duties the fifth man was also expected to double up in most of the other crew positions. He was also invaluable as the teamaker! Generally he was co-located alongside the driver and was given a machine gun which he could fire through a rudimentary vision block. As there were no proper sighting arrangements, the vision and firing areas were extremely limited, and the effectiveness of this particular weapon system was questionable.

The Soviet Union quickly gave up the fifth man and the KV 85 was their last five-man tank. In this respect they have led the world and as they were the first to reduce to a four-man crew so they have been the first to reduce to a three-man crew in conventional turreted tanks with the latest version of the T64.

The Germans remained committed to a five-man crew throughout the Second World War and it was not until they introduced Leopard 1 in 1965 that the crew size was reduced to four. Similarly the Americans, with some exceptions, persevered with the five-man crew right through until the M48 came into service in 1952.

The British were also firmly wedded to a five-man complement, although in some tanks that had been upgunned, such as Crusader 3 (57 mm), they had been forced to accept a three-man crew because the available space under the armour had become limited. Even Comet, introduced in 1945 as a successor to the upgunned Cromwell, still retained a five-man complement. When it was decided to abandon the Cromwell-Comet line of succession and develop an entirely new concept based on the lessons learnt during the Second World War it was apparent that if the tank was to have a sloped glacis plate; to be able to accommodate all the new equipment there would not be room for the fifth crew man. By then the need for the fifth man was being questioned and certainly the elimination of this crew position eases the designer's problems.

BATTLE TANKS

Most modern main battle tanks still have a crew of four, although the Russian T72 utilises an autoloader and only has a three-man crew, as does the unconventional Swedish "S" tank. A conventional four-man crew consists of a commander, gunner, loader/radio operator and driver.

Before considering any possible combination of tasks it is important to consider the role of the commander in the tank. In peacetime it is often easy to suspect that he is not used to his full capacity. In training he will be concerned with bringing the crew inside the tank up to the required standard and as a realistic fire and movement exercise is necessarily limited, he should have ample time available to supervise closely the various crew functions. This can lead to a feeling that the commander should undertake other tasks, but under battle conditions a very different picture emerges.

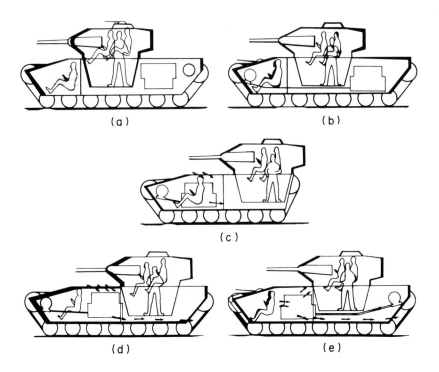

Fig. 8.1 Some typical tank layouts (360° traverse)

In battle the commander must be able to monitor continuously the tactical picture
whether the tank is in contact or not. Such a tactical awareness is essential if
he is to react to orders swiftly and correctly or if he is to interpret events correctly. His ability to do this relates directly to the tank's chance of survival.
Once the tank is in contact with the enemy he must then use his skill and with the
help of whatever equipment he has been given acquire targets to pass on to the
gunner to engage and destroy. This must be done whilst dealing with the normal
two-way passage of information, supervising the crew and in particular guiding
the driver when moving or taking up a new fire position.

POSSIBLE COMBINATIONS

Commander and Gunner

We have already seen that it is important to reduce the volume under armour in
order to bring down the total weight of the vehicle and one of the most attractive
ways is to reduce the crew size to three. The simplest way to achieve this is to
combine the tasks of two of the crew members or to reapportion the tasks of the
disposed crew member. There are six possible crew combinations, although some
are not really practical possibilities. The most attractive combination is the com-
mander/gunner concept. In many modern tanks most of the gunner's controls are
already duplicated at the commander's station and he has the ability to fire the
main armament. When there is a gunner the commander acquires the target, and

then there is a time lapse as he hands it over to the gunner to carry on the engagement. Time can be saved if the commander himself fires the main armament. If
this combination is adopted it means that the commander cannot acquire other
targets whilst the gunner is engaging the one previously acquired. Many of the
commander's tasks as mentioned previously cannot be undertaken simultaneously
with his responsibilities as the gunner, so the overall result is a net loss in efficiency and hence a probable reduction in survivability.

Commander and Loader

The commander/loader combination is perfectly acceptable for vehicles where the
weight of the main armament ammunition is such that the commander can load it
very easily, preferably with one hand. It is immediately apparent that this is completely out of the question for main battle tanks, and although within limits for
calibres up to the 76-90-mm range it is still likely to increase engagement times
and reduce the rate of fire. It is a solution most often found in reconnaissance
vehicles where firepower does not have the overriding priority it has in the main
battle tank.

Commander and Driver

The commander/driver combination in a conventional turreted tank is a non-starter,
as the commander would be unable to fulfil any of his functions from the driver's
station in the hull. If the driver's station is moved to the turret, the combination
is worth examining, but the argument that the commander cannot command while
he is driving the vehicle is still valid. It would be extremely difficult to fire the
gun whilst the vehicle was on the move, particularly if the target required that
the gun and turret need to be traversed away from the general direction in which
the vehicle was travelling. If, however, the gun is not free to traverse in relation
to the hull, as in the "S" tank, some of the objections are overcome. Indeed, within
the tactical limitations imposed by a fixed gun configuration, the "S" tank solution
whereby the commander and the gunner have identical driving control units seems
to be acceptable.

THE CONVENTIONAL TURRETED TANK

It has been generally accepted since the Second World War that a central turret
position was best suited for a main battle tank design, but within this constraint
there are several possibilities. The most common arrangement is for the driver
to be seated in the front, as shown in Fig. 8.1(a); behind him is a central fighting
compartment with a turret on it; finally the engine and transmission compartment
are to the rear. This presupposes that the tank has rear sprocket drive, but in
some configurations, notably the American Sherman series, the drive was through
a front sprocket necessitating a complex drive shaft from the rear engine compartment under the floor to the front final drives. This particular configuration as
shown in Fig. 8.1(b) was evolved as a result of the decision to utilise the well-
tried and proven Wright Whirlwind 9 Cylinder 340 hp radial aircraft engine, although
the diagram shows a conventional tank engine. As might be expected of an aero-
plane engine it had a very good power-to-weight ratio but posed considerable
installation problems leading to a very high tank.

As the engines were air cooled and the central power take-off was at a considerable
height above the lowest part of the engine, it was only really possible to fit the
engine at the very rear of the vehicle. Although this gave easy access for main-

tenance or engine replacement it did preclude the use of a rear sprocket drive and led to the adoption of a long transmission drive to the front sprocket.

The central turret position gives the best balance of features, allowing the driver a good view, full 360 degree traverse and the possibility of giving the gun a full 10-degree depression without unduly raising the height of the turret. Its major drawback is that with the modern requirement for high energy tank guns and the consequent large size of ammunition the volume needed under armour in the fighting compartment is ever increasing. This not only increases the overall size and weight of the tank but also tends to increase the target area presented by the turret. Most designs have been directed towards reducing the target size while still retaining the power and efficiency of a conventional tank design.

The Americans have made great efforts to reduce the size of the M60 turrets and when the 152-mm gun/launcher system became available they took advantage of this compact weapon system to reduce the frontal area. The prototypes were designated M60 A1E1 and M60 A1E2, but although the M60 A2 production version first appeared in 1966 it was not deployed until 1974 due to technical difficulties with the weapon system. It can be seen from Fig. 8.2 that both the gunner and loader are well down and almost below the turret ring, although the commander's position is still retained in a separate rather high cupola. Although this arrangement is sometimes referred to as a "cleft" turret, it is not really so in the traditionally accepted sense of the term.

Fig. 8.2 M60 A1E1

CLEFT TURRET

The true cleft turret should not be confused with the needle nose shape of the American M60 A1E1. The true cleft turret has a shape rather as if one had taken half an orange, placed it flat on a plate and then pressed a pencil down into it so that the top of the orange was level with the pencil. The sketch in Fig. 8.3 gives some idea of how this looks.

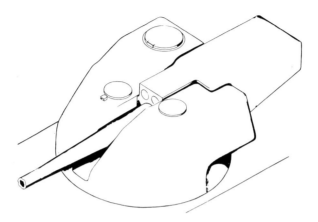

Fig. 8.3 Cleft turret diagram

Advantages

The particular advantage that this system bestows is that the gun can depress fully without the constraint of a turret roof. If the height of the turret roof, or strictly speaking the height of the turret either side of the cleft for the gun, can be reduced, then the weight of armour required to provide the desired level of protection is also reduced. As the breech of the gun is lying in a valley between either side of the turret it is afforded some measure of protection.

Disadvantages

By the very fact the cleft affords the gun some protection it also causes some design problems: it becomes as difficult to allow the gun the normal amount of elevation as it is to give a gun 10-degree depression in a conventional turret: in this case the turret ring immediately below the gun limits the elevation. As the gun is now dissociated from the crew, loading and servicing is difficult. An external autoloader becomes an essential element and care must be taken to ensure that the elevation of the gun is not obstructed by spent cases. Because servicing the gun presents a problem, reliability becomes of paramount importance.

As the gun is lying in a cleft of the turret the gun recoil is not constrained by the turret ring diameter. This can lead to a smaller tank, as we have already seen in Chapter 3. However, by its very nature the gun tends to divide the turret into two distinct halves which can lead to crew control problems and makes exchange of crew duties difficult if not impossible.

In the larger calibres, the weight savings are negligible and the 16-tonne American

T92 was one of the few tanks to get beyond the drawing board into prototype. In the end the need for an airborne tank which only mounted a relatively small calibre gun disappeared with the increased reliability of anti-tank guided weapons and the vehicle never went into production. It is not impossible to imagine a cleft turret AFV in the future, but it is unlikely.

OSCILLATING TURRET

Examples

The Germans are generally credited with being the first nation to produce a vehicle with an oscillating turret. This design was chosen for their 30-mm twin-gun anti-aircraft Kugelblitz tank, but it was not followed by any other designers until it appeared in the French AMX 13 tank and the Panhard armoured car.

In essence, the oscillating turret is a two-piece turret where the bottom half allows 360-degree rotation on a conventional turret ring race, but the upper part is mounted on trunnions at either side of the turret. The gun is fixed to the upper part of the turret and thus gun elevation or depression is obtained by tilting the whole of the upper turret.

After the Second World War, when the French still had considerable overseas interests, they decided to develop an air transportable light tank. At the time there were not any suitable air freighters in service, but some were projected that would be capable of lifting approximately 15 tonnes. In the event the AMX 13 was never used as an air portable tank, but its 75-mm high-velocity gun made it a very effective tank destroyer. Although the protection offered would not be acceptable by modern standards, in 1949, when the first prototype appeared, the level of protection was comparable with some main battle tanks still in service. As a light and highly mobile vehicle it offered a relatively inexpensive but effective solution that found favour in some nineteen countries. Later variants for the French army mounted a 90-mm gun, and a 105-mm version is available for export. Development towards its use as an MBT has now ceased.

Advantages

The advantage from this system accrues from the gun being fixed in relation to the upper turret. The sighting and fire control system are greatly simplified as there is no need to instal complex linkage between gun and sight, since both are tied to the upper turret and move in conjunction. As the gun is fixed to the upper turret the swept volume requirement inside the turret due to the elevation and depression of the gun is also greatly reduced.

The gun can be mounted close to the turret roof so it reduces the frontal area that must be presented to the enemy when engaging a target with the main armament. Because the gun is fixed in relation to the upper turret the configuration lends itself to an autoloader. Indeed, with the possibility of the upper turret oscillating rapidly in relation to the lower turret, a human loader would have a very difficult task and an autoloader is almost essential so that the loader's position can be eliminated.

The attraction of a relatively simple autoloader is lost if the magazine is positioned anywhere except in the bustle where the ammunition maintains a constant relative position to the gun and breech. Problems then arise in light tanks where there is a limit to the size of the amount of readily available ammunition. Such ammunition

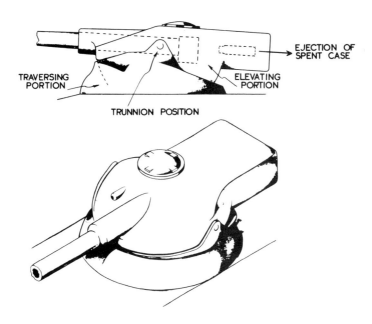

Fig. 8.4 Oscillating turret

magazines are generally replenished from the outside, and if the magazine has a relatively small capacity the need to expose the crew to replenish the ammunition could be a serious disadvantage for a tank involved in a fluid mobile battle, though it is not of such critical importance for a tank destroyer.

Disadvantages

Apart from problems of the amount of ready ammunition that can be stowed there are also the weight problems when the design is translated to vehicles in the MBT class. The sheer weight of the upper turret necessitates very substantial pivoting trunnions on either side of the turret. These in turn have to be supported by a substantial thickness of metal in an area where the protection levels would not necessarily dictate such a thickness.

As the gun is elevated, the upper turret has to be designed so that the lower skirt, which becomes exposed, offers the same amount of protection as if the turret were level. The skirt does nothing for the protection of the vehicle; when the gun is level it is down below the level of the turret ring. Similarly there must be a double skirt at the rear, but as the protection levels are lower, the weight penalty is not so severe.

NBC protection is particularly difficult to provide on an oscillating turret. Practically all AFVs rely upon crew compartment overpressure as a primary line of defence. Although this presupposes a certain amount of leakage to maintain the integrity of the system, the gross leakage caused by the inability to effectively seal the upper and lower turrets renders it impossible to utilise a collective NBC protection system.

It is also suggested that movement of the upper turret skirt behind the lower turret apron makes it vulnerable to "pinning" by the projectiles that fail to achieve penetration but manage to jam the turret so that it cannot be elevated or depressed.

To provide the protection at maximum elevation the curved skirt must necessarily have a large swept volume, making it difficult to make full use of the fighting compartment. A minor complication is the transfer of various services from the hull to the upper turret and vice versa. There is still a need for the rotary base junction between the lower turret and the hull, but there is also a need for a second set of slip rings between the upper and lower turret.

The apparent advantages of low tactical height and simplified sighting systems are soon outweighed by increasing weight penalties if MBT protection levels are imposed: the United States T69 experimental medium tank utilising an oscillating turret was abandoned in the late fifties. It would seem that this concept is only suitable for light vehicles where there is no attempt to provide MBT levels of protection.

DRIVER IN TURRET

Advantages

If the driver can be removed from the hull, then certain constrictions no longer apply. The turret can be brought forward as the space the driver previously occupied in front of the turret ring is no longer required. If the turret is forward it becomes much easier to achieve 10-degree depression without the need for unnecessarily high trunnions. This in turn should lead to a reduction in the hull height because the driver is no longer the limiting factor on hull height.

Fig. 8.5 US/FRG MBT70

Due to the height of the driver position in the turret it generally allows him an excellent view whether opened up, with his head and shoulders above the hatch, or closed down and using his vision devices. This can be a considerable help to the tank commander, as he does not now need to give as much guidance to the driver as before, particularly at night or in difficult terrain. If the driver is placed forward in the turret and the commander to the rear in a superior position, all is well if the tank is travelling forward with the gun forward. Once we start to traverse the turret but still require to drive the tank forward the problems arise.

Disadvantages

First and foremost, it is obviously necessary to provide a contra-rotating system for the driver so that he is always facing forward in a direct relationship to the hull. All the controls and instruments that the driver requires to perform his task relate to operations within the hull compartments and thus signals have to be transferred through the hull–turret interface, the rotary base junction and a second interface between the turret and the driver's independent contrarotating control console. This inevitably leads to complications.

As the turret rotates, keeping the driver facing forward, further problems arise. A relatively minor problem is the driver's disorientation. Unless his position is exactly central, which is not feasible because of the gun, he moves in relation to the hull, which makes it difficult to drive the vehicle precisely. A more serious problem arises over the allocation of the arcs of vision. It is readily apparent that it is not possible to give both the commander and the driver all-round vision and one or the other must accept that his vision will be blocked over certain arcs.

Having all members of the crew in the turret fighting compartment does help with the sharing of the crew duties and prevents any member of the crew being isolated; but this is a small compensation for the complexity of the system. The United States and Germany embarked on a joint venture to produce the MBT 70 which had such a configuration; it involved the use of 88 electrical and 11 hydraulic slip rings in the rotary base junction! Such complexity inevitably leads to high cost and coupled with doubts about the 152-mm "Shillelagh" gun/missile system led to its cancellation as a joint venture. The United States endeavoured to continue the development of this concept with XM 803, but escalating costs and continuing technical problems forced them to abandon the project.

EXTERNAL GUN

Reduction of Silhouette

Of all the unconventional concepts considered so far, the external gun shows the most promise. If the crew can be contained entirely below the turret ring then their chances of survival are obviously enhanced. In the purist form of the concept the gun is mounted on a plinth which is itself mounted on a rotating platform. Thus the target presented when engaging the enemy is remarkably small. As the gun is entirely supported by the external trunnions the height of the turret roof does not come into the calculations and the tactical height of the tank can be considerably reduced.

Weight Advantages

In Fig. 8.6 a typical weight analysis shows that the total percentage weight of armour is about 46% and the weight of the turret can be 75% of this armour weight.

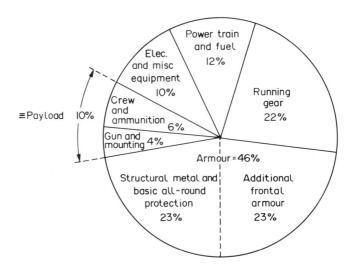

Fig. 8.6 Typical weight analysis — main battle tank

Any savings that can be made in this area will have a direct and significant effect
on the overall weight of the tank.   As a large percentage of the turret weight
is due to the need to provide protection for whatever volume is to be enclosed,
an external gun mounted on a rotating platform offers considerable savings in the
weight normally required for turret crew protection.   It is generally accepted
that such a system would lead to a smaller and lighter vehicle compared with a tank
mounting a gun of comparable calibre; this is well illustrated in Fig. 8.7.

The weight savings are very attractive, but several problems arise, notably from
the exposed and remote position of the main armament in relation to the crew compartment which is now below the turret ring.   The gun must be served by an autoloader, and as this must be tied directly to the ordnance it calls into question
the level of protection to be afforded.   If normal MBT levels are to be applied,
then the weight advantages will soon be lost and the fire control systems needed
to drive the gun will become large; indeed the inertia in the system will cause
problems for the gun control systems designers.

Automatic Loading

Any automatic loading system attached to the ordnance is likely to have a limited
capacity, and this then raises problems of replenishment.   Manual replenishment
is extremely undesirable, so some form of automatic reloading is required which
invites further complication.   Most autoloading systems can provide a choice of
two natures of ammunition relatively easily, but providing for any choice above
that becomes complex.   If the autoloader is accessible to the crew, manual loading of the additional natures is possible, but with a remote externally mounted gun
is not feasible.

The exact autoloading system chosen by the designer will depend on a number of
factors, but whichever option is selected it is almost certain that there will be some
out-of-balance problems as the ammunition is used.   This throws a greater strain
on the gun control system, not just in the power required but also because it
becomes difficult to stabilise.

Fig. 8.7 Bofors external gun on Marder chassis

Importance of Reliability

The reliability of the system becomes paramount because servicing the system on the battlefield is impossible except during a lull in the fighting. The obvious location for the machine gun is co-located in the weapon pod alongside the main armament. This raises even greater problems of access and, to date, machine guns are not noted for their reliability.

Most machine guns are fed by either belts or boxes of ammunition which require replacement when they are exhausted. Some vehicles already mount external machine guns for use by the vehicle commander, but these are not required to produce the same volume of fire that is expected from the coaxial machine gun. Fighter aircraft experienced a similar problem, particularly in the small calibre machine guns. If it is essential to have support from this type of weapon system it may be necessary to duplicate it.

Sighting

Perhaps the greatest problem to overcome is the design of suitable sighting and vision systems. With the crew below the turret ring line and the gun trunnions a metre above them the situation is something akin to the position of a submarine commander and his crew. It is difficult, but by no means impossible, to devise a gun-sighting system with a sight head either alongside or just below the gun barrel. However, it becomes even more difficult to provide all-round vision for the commander. It is essential that he is provided with a means to view the battle-field not only so that he can acquire targets but also that he can gather intelligence and be in a position to make the necessary decisions to fight the vehicle effectively. Although not so vital to the effectiveness of the tank, but just as important for its survival, is the need for some vision arrangements to assist the driver when the vehicle is moving in reverse. Normally this is achieved by the commander using the vision devices in his cupola, but if that is not available it may be necessary to provide a special vision device for the driver or another member of the crew.

With the advances in optronics and the introduction of free sights that are no longer mechanically linked to the gun, the problems associated with designing a sighting system are considerably eased. The incentives for success are great and it is not unreasonable to expect to be able to mount a 105-mm gun on a chassis similar to that of a MCV weighing approximately 25 tonnes.

FORWARD ENGINE AND TRANSMISSION

In the very early designs the engine was placed centrally. Consequently the centre of gravity was in the middle of the vehicle. It also allowed easy access for maintenance. As designs progressed it became advantageous to place the driver in the most forward position and to allocate the central position to the fighting compartment. A rear engine normally led to a rear sprocket design, but sometimes other factors, such as the design of available engines as in the Sherman, led to a design incorporating a rear engine but forward transmission and front sprocket drive.

Roles for which Forward Engine is Desirable

If easy access is a high priority, such as in an APC, then it becomes essential to mount the engine and transmission in the forward position. In light vehicles, where the power pack is comparatively small, it is relatively easy to locate it forward of the fighting compartment with the driver either alongside, as in the British CVR(T) series, or behind the engine compartment, as we can see from Fig. 8.8.

If it is intended to produce a series of vehicles based on the same chassis, then the forward engine and transmission configuration has a very strong attraction. Apart from the MBT, most other armoured fighting vehicles derive strong benefits from a forward engine configuration. When we turn to a MBT family, the recovery vehicle would like an unencumbered rear working compartment to house a winch and allow direct rear access. It has obvious advantages compared with the engineering problems associated with placing the winch in a central compartment. In that case the winch rope must be led over the top of the hull and it is difficult for the winch operator to be positioned so that he can see the vehicle casualty and be protected at the same time.

If it is intended to use the chassis as a basis of a self-propelled (SP) gun, then the forward engine configuration becomes even more advantageous. When a SP gun is firing there is a component of the firing forces which is transmitted along a line of action which is an extension of the gun barrel. In a tank these forces are relatively easily absorbed by the comparatively heavy weight of the vehicle. In a SP gun the forces are much greater and the vehicle relatively lighter. If the component force falls outside the ground plan of the vehicle then the vehicle will need some extra support in the form of a spade or other such aid to help support the firing forces. This is generally considered to be a small price to pay for the considerable advantage of rear access. When large amounts of ammunition are used, easy loading access becomes a prime consideration. A SP gun with rear access allows loading into the floor of the fighting compartment at most gun traverse positions. Loading into the rear of the turret can also be undertaken over a wide arc of turret traverse. On the other hand, positioning the fighting compartment in the centre of the vehicle inevitably requires the ammunition to be raised at least

Fig. 8.8 Alvis CVR(T) Scorpion

turret ring height before it can be loaded, and even then rear turret loading will
be restricted to certain turret traverse positions.

It is in the range of medium and light AFVs that the forward engine location finds
most favour, as it is in these weight classes that vehicles are designed from inception as part of a family of vehicles. The advantages of unrestricted rear access
for personnel carriers, ambulances and command vehicles are immediately apparent.
Rear access for a command vehicle does allow an extension to be fixed easily onto
the rear of the vehicle. This can considerably enlarge the available command area
and makes it much easier to function as a headquarters when the vehicle is stationary. It is normal practice for this extension area to be constructed of a light
tubular frame and covered with a waterproof fabric. Any form of ballistic protection is not really practicable, so such a system obviously has its limitations and
it must be possible to withdraw quickly and easily into the relative security of the
vehicle to continue the command function.

Forward Engines for MBTs

Placing the engine and transmission forward of the fighting compartment will increase
the protection provided for the crew, as the path length which any form of armour-

piercing projectile has to travel is greatly increased. If this path happens to be
through the transmission or engine, then the mobility is likely to suffer. The prime,
and currently only, example of this design in the MBT class is the Israeli Merkava,
as seen in Fig. 8.9. This design has been dominated by the need for crew survivability and placing the crew compartment to the rear obviously enhances this. It
brings other advantages in its wake which all add to the numerous small factors
which contribute to the chance of surviving.

Such a design allows access to the crew compartment through a clam-shell door
in the rear of the hull, which makes ammunition loading a simple task. It also allows
relatively protected access to the tank without the need for the crew to climb over
the top of the turret. When a tank is in a defensive position for any length of
time and there is a need for the crew to leave and enter the vehicle such access
must help improve crew survivability. The large crew compartment that this design
allows must be a bonus. Although it would be possible for a small infantry section
to be carried for a short time in considerable discomfort the greatest advantage
that this space bestows is the ability to carry a considerable quantity of ammunition.
Not only is the normal complement of ammunition said to be considerably greater
than other contemporary MBTs, the extra space allows for a special increment to
be stowed to meet the initial onslaught in any battle when ammunition usage rates
are notoriously high.

Until some of the limitations are examined it would seem surprising that anyone
would choose anything other than a forward engine configuration for a MBT. The
main problem is to arrange for the gun to have 10-degree depression without placing
the trunnions inordinately high and so raise the height of the tank. The more
the turret is to the rear of the vehicle the more difficult it becomes to obtain 10-
degree depression easily.

With the fighting compartment to the rear of the engine and transmission in most
battle positions, the optical sight path of the gun sights will cross these compartments
and the rising heat can cause optical problems. They are not insoluble but just
add to the designer's difficulties. One of the major problems lies with the balance
of protection, as the frontal surface area to be protected is so much larger than
a tank with a central turret.

The engine and transmission certainly provide protection, but only at the expense
of their own vulnerability. If they are to be protected adequately, then there is
a far greater surface area to be protected fully than compared with a rear engine
tank where the protection levels can be comparatively low. Inevitably it must add
to the weight of the tank.

If the fighting compartment is at the very rear of the vehicle, such as in some SP
guns, then this is far from ideal for a stable cross-country ride. The pitching
movements can be quite severe and make it very difficult to fight the vehicle
on the move. Not only are the crew discomfort levels fairly high but the burden
placed on the gun control equipment, particularly the stabilisation, may become
unacceptably high.

FIXED GUN

The concept of fixing the gun to the chassis is very attractive because this would
then immediately offer a simple method of automatic loading and would also permit
a longer barrel to be used than would be possible in a turreted tank of comparative
size and weight.

The vehicle is essentially simpler as the complexity of a fully rotating turret is avoided

Fig. 8.9 Israeli Merkava

and because it is compatible automatic loading a three-man crew becomes viable,
with the consequent advantages of reduced interior volume and hence the possibility
of a smaller lighter vehicle. The only tank currently in production to utilise this
configuration is the Swedish Bofors "S" tank, and the diagram in Fig. 8.10 shows
the general arrangements and the crew stations.

The commander and gunner have control units with which they can both steer the
tank when driving and traverse and elevate when firing. These control units are
identical; thus if necessary either the commander or the gunner alone can fight
the tank without changing crew positions, making it a one-man tank in emergencies.

The wireless operator's control unit is intended only for driving the tank in reverse
and is connected mechanically to the gunner's steering control unit.

Because the gun is fixed in relation to the hull, the gun is aimed in azimuth by
traversing the whole vehicle. The steering system employed allows the traversing
velocity to be continuously variable, giving fine control of gun traverse rates.
Elevation is achieved by changing the relative positions of the front and rear road
wheels.

This is controlled electrohydraulically by the commander or gunner. Signals from
the angle transmitters activate a pump which is connected between the working
cylinders of the road wheels. The pump will operate until the tank has reached
the correct angle of elevation or depression.

The fixed gun tank offers the advantage of a lower silhouette because the gun can
be placed close to the turret roof. The design will normally allow for the glacis
to be given a very favourable slope and thus enhance the protection levels that
can be afforded.

The main problem faced by this design is the difficulty of firing on the move. It
is possible to design a computer based firing system that would allow the tank,
whilst still on the move, to sweep through an arc and fire when the target image
and the correct lay of the gun are coincidental, but the hazards of such a system
are obvious.

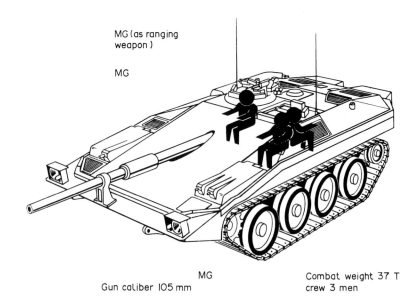

Fig. 8.10 "S" tank — general arrangements

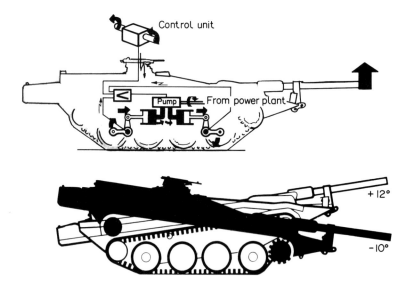

Fig. 8.11 "S" tank — method of gun elevation

A fixed gun solution can provide a very light and effective tank destroyer, but it cannot provide all the combat support roles that we currently demand of the main battle tank.

THE FUTURE

As the methods of defeating armour become more efficient, so the protection levels must rise. If the vehicle is to be kept within weight limits something must give; it is just not feasible to allow the weight to keep increasing. It is therefore likely that strenuous efforts will be made to produce a design that has a three-man crew with either an external gun or something akin to a cleft turret. Both solutions would offer considerable weight savings over a conventional tank offering the same levels of protection.

SELF TEST QUESTIONS

QUESTION 1   Name the two prime tasks of the crew of a main battle tank on the
              battlefield and indicate some of the subsidiary tasks.

              Answer   ....

                        ....

QUESTION 2   Why did most nations at the beginning of the Second World War
              consider a five-man tank crew essential?

              Answer   ....

QUESTION 3   What are the functions of the crew members in a conventional four-
              man tank?

              Answer   ....

                        ....

QUESTON 4   What are the three possible combinations of crew duties?

              Answer   ....

                        ....

QUESTION 5   What particular advantage does the cleft turret design bestow?

              Answer   ....

                        ....

QUESTION 6   Why is the oscillating turret design only suitable for light vehicles?

              Answer   ....

                        ....

QUESTION 7   Describe the major problems associated with the concept of placing
              the driver in the tank turret.

              Answer   ....

                        ....

QUESTION 8   What are the limitations of a forward engine design for a MBT?

              Answer   ....

                        ....

                        ....

QUESTION 9   What is the major problem with the fixed gun solution for a MBT?

Answer   ....

....

QUESTION 10   Why is it desirable to design a three-man MBT?

Answer   ....

....

....

Answers on page 225.

9. Infantry Armoured Vehicles

Scope

Previous chapters have described the historical development of the tank and the
technical factors that dictate its main design features. In this chapter we will
focus on Infantry Armoured Vehicles. (IAVs). We will review their historical
development, the roles that are assigned to units equipped with them, their consequent performance characteristics and requirements, and finally the main technical
factors that dictate their design features.

Terminology

There is much confusing terminology in this area which is due mainly to the variety
of roles in which these vehicles can be used. In some they are battlefield taxis,
providing mobility and protection to infantrymen who are delivered to a selected
dismounting area on the battlefield to fight on their feet. In others the vehicle
is itself considered a fighting element, a mobile protected platform from which the
infantry neutralise the enemy by firing their personal weapons through firing ports,
or a vehicle supporting infantry and destroying enemy vehicles with its own machine
guns and cannon. Finally, these vehicles, whether as armoured personnel carriers
or combat vehicles, are invariably used in supporting roles.

Figure 9.1 lists the terms that one is likely to meet in the literature on this subject. These terms differ in the emphasis they place on the use to which the vehicle
is put or on the type of infantry who will most probably use it.

The armoured personnel carrier (APC) is the oldest and traditional term used to
describe the vehicle embodied in the battlefield taxi concept. A complication with
this and with most of the other terms is that whenever an army buys one of these
vehicles, it always puts them to other uses. The basic APC will also come in variants
that can house command posts, carry certain weapon systems, such as anti-tank
guided missiles, transport and assist mechanics who perform vehicle recovery and
repair, and act as mobile ambulance. Some vehicle families extend to as many as
ten variants. Perhaps 50% of the vehicles in a mechanised battalion would be variants.
To call all of these vehicles APCs is thus rather misleading.

Terminology

APC	—	Armoured personnel carrier
MICV	—	Mechanised infantry combat vehicle
IAFV	—	Infantry armoured fighting vehicle
AIFV	—	Armoured infantry fighting vehicle
ICV	—	Infantry combat vehicle
IFV	—	Infantry fighting vehicle
MCV	—	Mechanised combat vehicle
MIV	—	Mechanised infantry vehicle
AIV	—	Armoured infantry vehicle
IAV	—	Infantry armoured vehicle

Fig. 9.1 List of terms used to denote IAVs

The next six terms place their emphasis on the fact that these types of vehicles are intended to be used directly in combat. They will probably have gun ports that permit their occupants to fire their personal weapons while riding in them. They will certainly have a combination of machine guns and cannons with which to provide fire support to their infantry and with which to engage and defeat the vehicles of the opposing infantry.

The next two terms focus on the type of infantry most likely to use the vehicle. Some armies, notably the West German, differentiate between infantry that merely ride onto the battlefield in armoured vehicles and fight dismounted, and those who accompany armour, fight with the armour from their vehicles, and dismount only when a particular tactical circumstance so demands. The former would be called mechanised infantry and the latter armoured infantry.   The panzergrenadiers of the Bundeswehr are armoured infantry and their vehicle, the Marder, is thus an armoured vehicle (AIV).

The last term is the most general. It contains no hidden assumptions about either the tactical concepts to be employed with the vehicle or the types of infantry that will use it. It also does not obscure the fact that in either case there will be variants that are neither personnel carriers nor fighting vehicles.

HISTORICAL DEVELOPMENT

First World War

The historical development of these vehicles closely paralleled that of the tank. Indeed the requirement for armoured personnel carriers was perhaps a somewhat more obvious one than that for the main battle tank in those heady days of 1916 and 1917 when mechanised warfare was first being thought about. In terms of design features and intended use, the first British armoured personnel carrier, the Mark V*, differs probably less from those of today than do the first tanks from their modern counterparts.

Fig. 9.2 Mark V* tank, an early APC

The obvious requirement was for a means of transporting infantry and supplies across a battlefield that contained obstacles, both natural and man-made, in the form of trenches and wire. As this battlefield was invariably covered by fire from rifles and machine guns, the need to provide protection against it was obvious.

Common sense then suggested that mounting some form of machine gun or cannon on these vehicles was useful. These ideas converged to produce the four basic characteristics of infantry armoured vehicles:

CAPACITY
MOBILITY
PROTECTION
FIREPOWER

The first British armoured personnel carrier, the Mark V* already mentioned, was developed from the Mark V tank by lengthening its hull, removing its main armament, replacing it with two machine guns and moving the engine forward.

The resulting vehicle could carry 50 infantrymen or 10 tons of supplies. A later development was the Mark IX tank which was a purpose-built APC, the first in the history of warfare.

Second World War

At the beginning of the Second World War two armies had armoured personnel carriers. Predictably the Germany Army as it embraced the ideas developed by JFC Fuller, Liddel Hart and Guderian, led the way with the Sdkfz 251, a picture of which is shown in Fig. 9.4.

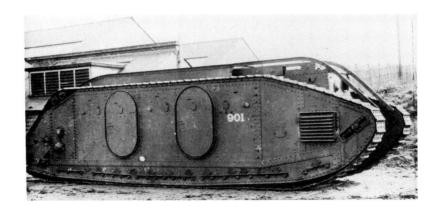

Fig. 9.3 Mark IX tank, the first purpose-built APC

Fig. 9.4 Sdkfz 251, the first German APC

The US Army produced a similar vehicle, the M3, half-tracked APC.

The armies of the British Commonwealth had a requirement for an APC thrust upon them in the Battle of Normandy. They met this requirement by removing the turrets from Churchill and Sherman tanks to produce Kangaroo tanks. They provided good mobility, a restricted capacity, and excellent protection from flat trajectory, but very little from overhead fire. They also provided rather a rough ride for their occupants while access and exit was extremely awkward. Figure 9.5 shows a Kangaroo tank used by British Commonwealth armies.

Fig. 9.5 A Kangaroo tank, used by British Commonwealth armies

The Development of Wheeled APCs

The possibility of putting light armour around a motor car suggested itself as soon
as these vehicles found their way into the military inventory. Indeed as early as
1908 armoured cars were seen on battlefields. They came to be used not only in
the reconnaissance role but in internal security and police anti-riot operations as
well. Armoured cars were used by T. E. Lawrence and figured in the uprisings
in the Russian Revolution. They continued in British service in the Middle East
and in India where use in internal security operations was their main role.

Their development continued in two directions. The first produced armoured reconnaissance cars, and the other produced wheeled APCs for use in internal security
operations, of which the AT 105 is an example (see Fig. 9.6).

The Advent of the MICV

Development has continued since the Second World War. The first Western postwar APCs were tracked, providing light armour and a machine gun in a non-powered
turret. Soviet development placed equal emphasis on wheels (BTR 50) and tracks
(BTR 60). The Soviets then produced a more formidable vehicle, the BMP.

The BMP is interesting for several reasons. While its armour is not particularly
thick, its effect was enhanced by using diesel fuel tanks in the rear doors as armour,
providing protection both against SA bullets and fragments and against nuclear
radiation. The most obvious feature of the BMP, however, is its significantly
enhanced firepower, in the form of a 73-mm low-pressure gun and a Sagger anti-
tank guided missile. Finally, the infantry were provided with firing ports, four
on each side, through which to fire their section weapons.

Fig. 9.6 AT105, a purpose-built IS APC

This vehicle is obviously much more than a battlefield taxi. It was designed to
carry its infantry on to an objective, provide direct fire support when they had
dismounted, and at all times provide anti-tank firepower of greater range than
an infantry section could at that time be expected to carry on its back. The BMP
does not provide really good ballistic protection. It cannot: the vehicle must float.
However, its designers have produced a remarkably low vehicle that undoubtedly
would be much less easy to hit than, say, a FV432 or M113. It thus provides
enhanced protection but indirectly. An important consequence of this low profile
is a cramped compartment for the infantry. Big tall infantrymen undoubtedly find
this vehicle highly uncomfortable.

The West German Marder was the first infantry fighting vehicle in NATO. Its main
features are a significantly increased level of armour protection and a gun specifically designed to engage and defeat enemy APCs. The vehicle cannot float, but
has a good capacity to wade.

The engagement of enemy APCs is a role that appears to have received less
attention than it deserves, although there is encouraging evidence that this situation is improving. The reasons for this are to a degree technical and to a degree
doctrinal; the mounting of an anti-APC gun on an APC poses some surprisingly
intractable problems to the infantry. These will be dealt with later on. However,
few armies appear to have assigned the requirement to engage enemy APCs and
ICVs a sufficiently high priority to produce organisations properly equipped and
oriented to assume the role effectively.

Fig. 9.7a Soviet IAV

Fig. 9.7b Soviet IAV

Fig. 9.7c Soviet IAV

The Ultimate IFV

The Israeli Merkava tank shown in Fig. 9.8 introduces a final possibility. This
tank has its engine in the front, thereby increasing the weight of metal between
its crew and the enemy. A consequence of this vehicle layout is rear loading doors
to a compartment in which extra ammunition can be carried. This additional space
can also be used to accommodate rescued crews from knocked out tanks and can
carry up to six infantrymen. While this space was originally designed for ammunition stowage, it does demonstrate that from a technical point of view it is possible
to build a vehicle having the mobility, protection and firepower of a tank, and the
capacity of an APC.

The Direct Fire Support Requirement

An additional theme can be traced intermittently throughout the history of the infantry armoured vehicle. The first tanks were essentially infantry direct fire support
(DFS) vehicles because the concept of a main battle tank (MBT) as we know it
today had simply not emerged. The great debate that raged between the First
and Second World Wars was a debate over whether armoured forces as such could
and should be organised. Up to the time where that point was established, all

Fig. 9.8 Israeli Merkava — the ultimate IFV?

seemed to agree that there was a requirement for a vehicle to operate in the DFS role. When the concept of the MBT was finally confirmed, the DFS role retreated as a separate entity, to be replaced by an infantry telephone on the back of the tank. Most modern tanks still have it. But as armoured forces become more specialised and more expensive, the DFS role assumes new prominence.

Many countries are now convinced of the requirement for a DFS vehicle. This vehicle is not a tank, as it is not designed to participate in offensive armoured operations. It is, however, employable as a tank destroyer as well as a mobile platform for a gun with which to provide intimate direct fire support to infantry who will give it protection against short-range anti-tank weapons when it is moving. The main features of these vehicles when compared with tanks are reduced armour protection and expense.

THE INFANTRY OF THE FUTURE

The advent of modern technology has had a significant impact on the way armies organise themselves. One of the most obvious results has been increasing role orientation, as training becomes more complex, protracted and expensive. The infantry, the Queen of Battle, is becoming a specialist.

The requirement for three separate types of infantry can be easily identified. Superimposed on these types are two additional roles. The three types of infantry can be called light, mechanised and armoured infantry. One of the two additional roles is the internal security (IS) role which is essentially a police function on which, typically, infantry are used; however, as the British Army's experience in Ulster

clearly indicates, this is a role in which any properly trained and adequately dis-
ciplined body of troops can be employed. The other additional role is the DFS role
itself.

It can, of course, be argued that this is not essentially an infantry role; it could
equally be an armoured corps task. However, most armies' armoured corps do not
want it. Thus if it is not taken on by the infantry as a role that must be fulfilled,
it will not be seen to exist by anyone else and will not be fulfilled by others.

LIGHT INFANTRY

Light infantry are the conventional infantry of this century. They march to battle
on their feet or are carried there by vehicles not integral to their battalions. Their
supporting weapons such as mortars and anti-tank guided missiles are mounted
on wheeled vehicles. Their command posts, ambulances and logistics vehicles are
also wheeled. Some of them may well be airborne and all are likely to be trained
to be transported on aircraft if not parachuted into battle.

From the point of view of employment they are the ideal strategic reserve of an
army. They are easily transported by fixed-wing aircraft over strategic distances,
and their rifle company groups can be transported by helicopters over tactical
distances. They can be effectively employed in defensive operations over the full
range of the spectrum of conflict, but are not suitable for offensive functions in
mechanised and armoured operations except for deep infiltration and tank hunting,
for which only infrequent opportunities are likely to arise. They are the ideal
selection for IS operations.

Light infantry can have rifle companies mounted in vehicles. In this case they
become motorised or lorried infantry. Consideration of expense and of their
requirement for protection and mobility suggest that their ideal vehicle would be
wheeled, thus having somewhat restricted cross-country mobility.

It would provide protection against small arms bullets at short range and against
shell, mortar bomb and grenade fragments, but not against the automatic cannon
that are becoming a more significant presence on the high intensity battlefield.
Increased protection would be a benefit for which the price in terms of expense
and strategic and tactical mobility would probably be too high.

MECHANISED INFANTRY

Mechanised infantry are the journeymen of high-intensity operations. They participate in the full range of tactical functions on the battlefield and can operate for
limited periods away from their vehicles. In defensive operations they are of particular significance because of their flexibility; this is a result of the high levels
of mobility and protection afforded them by their vehicles. All members of the
battalion are mounted. Those who will be in direct contact with the enemy, members
of rifle companies and forward command posts, and personal workers in the medical,
repair, recovery and supply functions, will operate from tracked vehicles.

Their vehicle is an armoured personnel carrier, not a combat vehicle. It must provide the same level of mobility afforded to tanks, with whom they must operate.
The vehicle must provide protection against small arms bullets and shell and mortar
bomb fragments, and in addition must provide some degree of protection against
the anti-APC cannon likely to be encountered on the battlefield. The vehicle must

be of sufficient size to permit its occupants to operate from it for at least 2 days
with resupply of rations and ammunition. Stormer is a modern mechanised infantry
vehicle.

Fig. 9.9 Stormer, a modern MIV

ARMOURED INFANTRY

Armoured infantry are gaining acceptance as a specialised form of infantry. The
German Army has had Panzergrenadiers for many years. They participate with
tanks as tactical elements integral to the armoured unit. They are usually able
to fire small arms from their vehicle which itself must be able to fight. Their tactical role is a supportive one. They promote the shock action of the armour by
protecting it when it rests and refits; they are useful when the unit moves through
defiles; they can take on enemy infantry armoured vehicles; they are essential
for consolidating the capture of objectives before moving on to continue the advance;
and finally they suppress enemy anti-tank weapons.

The armoured infantry vehicle must have the same mobility as do the tanks with
which it is to operate. It must provide a high level of protection, defeating all
anti-APC cannon on the battlefield. Ideally it would withstand the same levels
of attack as the tank, but considerations of expense, mobility and capacity make
this impracticable.

The fact that this vehicle must carry a cannon with which to engage and defeat
enemy infantry armoured vehicles is a major complication in its design. MCV80,
a new British vehicle, is a modern armoured infantry vehicle.

Fig. 9.10 MCV80, a modern AIV

THE INTERNAL SECURITY (IS) ROLE

The IS role also demands a protected vehicle. This vehicle must be able to manoeuvre easily in narrow streets, and will be used extensively, indeed primarily, on sur- faced roads and tracks. It should therefore be wheeled. It must permit its occu- pants to maintain a high level of surveillance over its surroundings. It must also permit them to use their personal weapons against anyone who takes a shot at them. An apparent capability to return this sort of fire acts as a deterrent. Indeed deterrence in this role is possibly more important than the actual effect of the fire available.

The vehicle perhaps more than others must permit very rapid entry and exit, pre- ferably from its sides as well as its rear. Access through the sides is only prac- ticable with wheeled vehicles. The vehicle must mount a machine gun.

THE DFS ROLE

The final type of infantry armoured vehicle is the DFS vehicle. This vehicle is essentially a platform for a gun that has a good capability against enemy tanks. The weapon must also, if it is to provide proper direct fire support, fire HE and anti-personnel rounds. Its mobility must be the equivalent of that of the APC for mechanised infantry with whom it will normally operate. Its protection should be as good as that of these vehicles. Higher levels of protection may not be worth providing since the vehicle will fire from ambush in the defence and as part of an all-arms team in offence.

This role is a definite requirement. Whether an army requires a specialised vehicle to perform it is another matter, since any MBT can do the job more than adequately. MBTs are extremely expensive because of the high levels of technology involved

Fig. 9.11 Swedish IKV 91, a DFS vehicle

in meeting their conflicting requirements for firepower, mobility and protection.
DFS vehicles are cheaper than MBTs because their requirements are less. There
may come a time in an army's calculations of the trade-offs between what it requires
and what it can afford that the DFS vehicle can be justified on economic grounds.
This is most likely to occur in an army that sees itself in an essentially defensive
posture ranged against a larger armour-heavy foe.

In a very real sense this vehicle is necessary because it is not worthwhile providing a very expensive main battle tank for a role in which its mobility and protection are not entirely necessary. A prime example is the Swedish IKV 91 tank
destroyer, a picture of which is shown in Fig. 9.11.

VARIANTS

All of the vehicles described above will require variants except the DFS vehicle.
It, of course, can be considered as, and in many actual examples is, simply a
variant of either an APC or an AIV.

Each of the three types of infantry requires a different set of variants of its basic
armoured carrier. While not all armies would agree on its detailed composition,
it is possible to produce a logical list of those variants by type of infantry. A
variety of factors including tactical concepts and budgetary constraints will determine which of these variants is actually produced for a particular army. Figure
9.12 lists these possible variants.

Variant	Type of Infantry		
	Light	Mechanised	Armoured
Infantry			
Section	x	x	x
Command	x	x	x
Mortar	x	x	
Anti-tank	x	x	
Anti-APC		x	x
Pioneer Dozer		x	x
Artillery observation post		x	
Artillery command		x	
Armoured engineer			x
Armoured bridge layer			x
Recovery	x	x	x
Vehicle repair		x	x
Ammunition			
Artillery		x	
Tank		x	x
Logistics	x	x	x
Ambulance	x	x	x

Fig. 9.12 Possible variants of IAVs for each type of infantry

THE BASIC CHARACTERISTICS OF INFANTRY ARMOURED VEHICLES

Early on in this chapter the four conventional characteristics of infantry armoured vehicles were introduced. They were:

CAPACITY
MOBILITY
PROTECTION
FIREPOWER

A little thought, however, will indicate that there are good reasons for changing two of these - Mobility and Protection. The terms that we will substitute will include more complex and more valid concepts.

When one considers the uses to which these vehicles are put, one has to note that mobility is a somewhat incomplete term. Certainly it is called for, but there are other related considerations as well. These include the reliability of the vehicle, the ease with which it is maintained and the ease with which it can be repaired. The importance of factors such as these in a vehicle which will be employed in mobile operations demands that they be given adequate recognition. A term such as Availability seems more likely to convey the essential connotation than does simple Mobility. We will use Availability throughout the rest of this chapter.

A thought about protection might suggest that more subtle considerations ought
to be included as well. The most important is that while protection is a key
ingredient, what the vehicle must really do is survive on the battlefield. We will
use Survivability throughout the rest of the chapter.

We will thus consider the following to be the basic characteristics of the infantry
armoured vehicle

CAPACITY
AVAILABILITY
SURVIVABILITY
FIREPOWER

THE RELATIVE IMPORTANCE OF THE BASIC CHARACTERISTICS

The relative importance assigned to each of these basic characteristics has a tremendous impact on the vehicle that is produced to meet the associated requirement. The examples that follow at Fig. 9.13 emphasise this point.

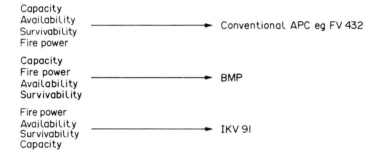

Fig. 9.13 The impact of changing the order of priority
of the basic characteristics of IAVs

FOUR SETS OF FUNDAMENTAL OPTIONS

Any army establishing a requirement for an IAV must not also assign a set of
priorities to the four basic characteristics; it must also make decisions on four
other basic questions. They are: should the vehicle have tracks or wheels?; is
priority to be given to firing ports or the basic internal seating arrangements?;
does it need to swim, ford or wade?; are weapon(s) to be mounted on the vehicle?

TRACKS VERSUS WHEELS

The decision between tracks or wheels is rather complex, more complex than perhaps it first appears. Some companies, notably in France, seem quite keen on
putting remarkably heavy guns on wheeled vehicles. The Soviet Union replaced
a tracked APC, the BTR 50, with a wheeled APC, the BTR 60, in their motor rifle
divisions in the 60s, and still use it.

Several factors predominate. The extent to which the vehicle will be used on surfaced roads and hard tracks is one factor tending to favour wheels if extensive

road use is anticipated. The density of the vehicle is another; one would not expect to see a 60 tonne main battle tank appear on wheels. The reliability and survivability of wheels is another. Multiwheeled vehicles can run with flat tyres or possibly missing a whole wheel station. A tracked vehicle cannot move with a cut track.

Generally speaking, tracked vehicles give better mobility, because they have lower mean maximum pressures than wheeled vehicles.

The more technical aspects of this matter were discussed in Chapter 7. Suffice it here to say that normally IS APCs are wheeled but most other IAVs are tracked. As the armour of these vehicles increases, as it certainly will if the increasing profusion of anti-APC cannon on the battlefield is to be countered, then in spite of advances in wheeled vehicle technology, mechanised and armoured infantry vehicles will continue to be tracked in the future.

FIRING PORTS AND SEATING ARRANGEMENTS

The requirement for firing ports is dictated by the role of the troops who will use the vehicle. Typically IS APCs such as Saracen or the AT 105 and AIVs such as Marder have firing ports. This requires that the troops sit in the vehicle facing outwards. Several quite significant results stem from this fact. Whether firing ports are worth having is itself quite a complex question. When one takes into account the fact that the vehicle will normally be moving when the firing ports are used, that the capacity of the infantrymen to detect and observe targets will be severely limited, and that the vehicle as a platform is bouncing, rocking and pitching in its cross-country movement, one can wonder whether the fire from firing ports is likely to be effective. At best it will be neutralising fire. That requirement might be more adequately met by light machine guns fired remotely and traversing over fixed arcs on either side of the vehicle.

Whether or not the infantrymen can fire effectively when facing outward, it is safe to say that when they are facing outward they have a better chance of maintaining some sense of orientation on the battlefield. How important that is is very much a matter of opinion. Some infantry company commanders recognise that when one sits an infantryman in a dark noisy vehicle that bounces him severely when it moves, he will tend to go to sleep or at least doze. Some will agree that there is nothing wrong with this, that it is a form of admittedly imperfect rest and that he will become alert quite quickly when he knows that he is approaching the objective or hears enemy fire. Others want their troops to remain alert throughout an approach march. This is more likely if they are facing outward.

Group solidarity is a factor too. With the section facing inward, hand signals and shouts are a possibility. Eye-to-eye communication is possible. So too, however, is the realisation that one's opposite number has just been hit by an armour-piercing bullet from a cannon. When troops are facing outward their feeling of solidarity is reduced as is the section commander's capacity to brief. Good discipline, training and sound drills can offset these disadvantages.

Access is not normally a factor at issue, as with proper design of the seating and doors, adequate access can normally be provided. That is not to say that all vehicles actually provide adequate access: some simply do not.

A final important factor is that in vehicles in which the troops face outwards there must be some form of superstructure in the centre. Fuel tanks are also sometimes located here. The existence of these structures severely limits the capacity of the vehicle when used for other functions such as command posts and ambulances.

This is perhaps the most significant point of all.

In a very few wheeled APCs the troops face forward. This familiar arrangement combines the best features of both other arrangements. Control and some orientation are possible. However, the requirement to provide an exit aisle to the rear means that some space is not efficiently used. As a consequence the vehicle is unlikely to be able to carry the requisite quantities of stores, ammunition and rations in this configuration.

SWIMMING, SNORKELLING AND WADING

Determining whether an infantry armoured vehicle should swim, snorkel or merely wade, is quite outside the scope of this chapter. We will deal here only with the consequence of the decision.

Many in-service IAVs swim; BMP, FV432 and M113 are examples. Marder, an armoured infantry vehicle, does not, and for a very good reason. Its gun, turret and armour produce a vehicle of such density that it will not float. This fact was obviously the result of a conscious decision.

Any IAV which provides significant protection against anti-APC cannon may snorkel if that is provided for, will obviously wade, but will only swim with the attachment of large swimming screens familiar to those who have read about the "DD" tanks used in the Normandy landings.

VEHICLE ARMAMENT

Expansion of the Vehicle Role

No aspect of IAVs has caused more discussion than the question of what weapon(s) to mount. The reason is straightforward. As soon as a weapon is mounted upon it, the vehicle becomes a gun platform and assumes a role that can conflict directly with its role as an armoured personnel carrier. The bigger the gun the greater is the conflict. At some stage the role of gun platform dominates, to the detriment of the role of personnel carrier.

Conflict is not the only complication. As the gun or guns become larger and more difficult to operate, they begin to impinge on the organisation of the infantry section, its rank structure and its training requirements.

The Effect of Mounting a Machine Gun

What types of weapons are we to consider? There will at least be a machine gun. Its role at the minimum is to provide some firepower for the immediate defence of the vehicle. It may be employed to deter enemy aircraft within range who are attacking the vehicle. It can also be used to provide supporting fire when the infantry in the vehicle have dismounted, either to attack or to occupy a defensive position. In either case a soldier will have to remain with the vehicle to man the gun. The restricted visibility of the driver means that he cannot man the gun; consequently a gunner who will also act as vehicle commander will have to remain with the vehicle. Thus two men must remain in the vehicle. This is a simple arrangement without further complications in organisation and training.

The Effect of Mounting a Cannon

But if we want to mount an anti-APC cannon such as the Rarden cannon or the American Hughes Chain Gun in 25 or 30 mm, the situation becomes more complex. The ammunition for these weapons costs in the order of £25 per round; it is heavy and bulky to store. They fire at rates varying from 100 to 600 rounds per minute; they must carry large amounts of ammunition, which competes for space in the vehicle. The gunner, to be effective against moving vehicles, must have significant initial training of perhaps 6 week's duration, and his skills must be kept sharp; he must have refresher training. He has become a specialist. Furthermore, if this gun is to be fired effectively and the vehicle commanded properly, we now have a three-man crew, who must remain with the vehicle. If the section on the ground is to remain at eight men, the recognised ideal, the vehicle must carry eleven men. The gun has increased the strength of the section. The vehicle commander must receive training in the tactical handling of the vehicle and in commanding his two subordinates. He is now an NCO. The section requires both a commander and a 2IC when dismounted; thus the cannon has increased the number of NCOs in the section from two to three.

Finally, the training requirements of the gunner are likely to be sufficiently complex that he cannot be taught his gunnery within the battalion. Everyone else in the section probably can. This is a significant complication in the training arrangements of a battalion.

In the circumstances of the DFS vehicle, these complications are less severe because there is no role conflict. The vehicle has one role and the company or platoon is organised around its role and its training requirements.

Tactical Conflicts

In an MIV the role conflict is most severe if an anti-APC gun is called for. Those locations from which the vehicle operates best when engaging enemy APCs are not likely to be the best from which to prepare to move the infantry section associated with that vehicle. One role may call for deployment covering an open flank, the other will require the vehicle to be tucked into a copse top the rear of the section. Resolution of these tactical conflicts can only be achieved at the expense of tactical effectiveness.

In armoured infantry the conflict is reduced because the vehicle operates as a fighting vehicle. When the infantry dismount, it follows along to support them, benefiting also from the firepower of the tank forces in the immediate vicinity.

The only satisfactory way to avoid this role conflict in mechanised infantry vehicles is to separate the roles. This is best done by providing an anti-APC platoon in the battalion, a sister of the anti-tank platoon, equipped with a vehicle such as Scimitar to engage enemy APCs. APCs can then be left to do what they do best – move infantrymen about the battlefield. The objection to this is simply a matter of expense.

CAPACITY

The first APCs, those of the First World War, carried about 50 men, a platoon's worth in those days, or 10 tons of stores. The APCs of the Second World War carried far fewer, possibly 5 or 6 up to 12. Today the infantry armoured carrier must be designed to provide a capacity for a variety of contents and functions.

Figure 9.14 shows the basic components of capacity for a typical infantry section
vehicle and outlines those when the vehicle is used as a support vehicle.

Crew

Communications equipment

Combat supplies (rations, water and ammunition)

APC vehicle   Support vehicle

Dismounting infantry   Support functions (various)

Section stores and equipment   Function stores and equipment
                                                        (various)

Rucksacks
Picks and shovels
Weapons
Mines and associated stores
Wire and associated stores
Surveillance equipment

Fig. 9.14 Components of capacity in IAVs

The requirement for the infantry section vehicle takes precedence for two reasons.
It will be the most numerous, outnumbering any other variant by probably at least
10 to 1. Secondly, it is the most demanding in terms of volume; thus having
provided for its requirement, one can also provide adequately, if not ideally,
for any other function. The converse is not true.

The size of the dismounting section is generally the main determinant of capacity.
However, when one mounts an anti-APC gun on an infantry armoured carrier, the
conflict in roles is translated into a conflict over space. With care this conflict
can, of course, be resolved.

The addition of one man to the section increases the requirement for space, not
only for him, but also for his rucksack or pack, his rations, his water, and his
ammunition. There is also clearly an upper limit to the capacity that can be provided. This limit is determined by the allowable width of the vehicle and other
technical considerations dealt with in previous chapters.

One can see that the section vehicle becomes a general repository for a great variety
of items: it is the section's "golf bag".

The same general technical constraints encountered in providing armour protection
for tanks prevail in IAVs. The difference is that capacity is a fundamental requirement, not an implied one as in tanks. The levels of armour protection called for
are significantly lower, though they are rising. Thus accommodating the requirement for capacity tends to be easier.

AVAILABILITY

The early APCs understandably were not reliable, so their availability was low,
but the quite spectacular improvements in automotive engineering over the years
has produced predictable improvements in the availability of infantry armoured
carriers. Figure 9.15 indicates the main components of availability, each of which
in turn is a fairly complex quality.

Mass of vehicle
Size of vehicle
Nominal ground pressure
Mean maximum pressure
Mobility of vehicle across country and on roads,
    tracks and streets
Availability relative to tanks
Mobility when suspension system damaged
Water-crossing capability
Through-snow capability
Reliability
Maintainability
Repairability

Fig. 9.15 Components of availability in IAVs

It is obvious that there can be no absolute measure of availability. However, there
are measures of many of its components; for example, figures for mean time between
failures can be applied to the suspension and propulsion systems. As a result
specifications of availability understandably contain as many precise indices of its
components as is possible, and then add statements on performance relative to some
other vehicle. Thus even if an absolute figure cannot be quoted, a comparison
with the performance of another vehicle can be stipulated.

The requirement for availability differs somewhat in the three general types of
infantry armoured carriers that we have identified. The most strenuous requirement is that for the AIV. This vehicle must in general terms be able to go everywhere the tanks it is to accompany can go. To say everywhere is perhaps over-
stating the case. Tanks with their high density and power-to-weight ratio can
crash through buildings and trees. It is neither a requirement nor a possibility
that an AIV could match a main battle tank in this sort of going because it will not
have the same density as the tank, even though it may have a similar power-to-
weight ratio. The real requirement is for a capability to keep up with tanks in
their normal functions, that is when they are engaged in fire and movement on
the battlefield. This is a technical challenge that can be met.

The availability of mechanised infantry vehicles is not so important as that of AIVs.
This is fortunate, because it will almost certainly be lower. AIVs tend to be less
dense and, regardless of their power-to-weight ratio, simply will not have the
same cross-country performance as tanks. However, conversely, they are likely
to be better in water-crossing. For operations in snow they will tend not to be
as good as tanks because, having less ground clearance, they tend to belly up
more easily.

For light infantry in IS operations, the requirement for availability is less, and
within availability different emphasis is placed on the components. Indeed the
effective difference in these requirements is to a degree one of emphasis rather
than of absolute requirement.

SURVIVABILITY

Survivability is easily the most complex of the basic characteristics of IAVs. This
stems from a very straightforward consideration. If we think of the vehicle as
a target for a weapon system of any type, then the probability of surviving an
attack, an inverse function of the familiar single-shot kill probability associated
with the weapon system, is the product of several components. These components
are:

1.   Probability of avoiding detection increased; for example, by a low silhouette
     or good camouflage.

2.   Probability of avoiding engagement on being detected increased; for example,
     by overloading the engagement capabilities of the enemy force.

3.   Probability of surviving an engagement increased; for example, by thickening
     the armour.

A little reflection will indicate that there are both active and passive measures that
one can take to increase survivability. An obvious active measure is to move so
that engagement is difficult. A passive measure would be thickened armour.

Further reflection will also indicate that there are direct and indirect approaches.
Direct approaches deal with the probability of surviving an engagement, while indirect methods affect the probabilities of detection and engagement. Figure 9.16
summarises these considerations.

	Direct	Indirect
Active	"Active" armour NBC collective air filters Adopting hull-down positions whenever possible Driver alertness and skill	Increased speed and agility Improved camouflage Swamping enemy's engagement capabilities Driver training Headlights
Passive	Thickened armour against both projectiles and nuclear radiation Seat belts and padding	Smoke grenade projectors Small size as a target Reduced radar and IR image

Fig. 9.16 Complexity of survivability

Survivability thus implies a complex array of attack agencies. These range from
the anti-APC cannon through nuclear radiation to vehicle accidents.

The relative emphasis that one assigns to these various attack agencies determines
the survivability of the various vehicles for the three types of infantry. Thus
NBC agents and anti-APC cannon would not be emphasised in a light infantry carrier
for IS operations whereas they would dominate in the AIV.

FIREPOWER

The first APCs had machine guns, and virtually every IAV since has had some
weapon or other. Common sense seems to dictate that no vehicle of this sort
should ever be incapable of engaging at least enemy soldiers on their feet, though
the incidence of use of these weapons may be relatively low. The full range of
targets for weapons to be mounted on IAVs varies in complexity from enemy soldiers
in the open to enemy APCs and tanks to helicopters and fixed wing aircraft.

The tactical and organisational implications of mounting anti-APC weapons on these
vehicles have already been discussed, but the problems of mounting weapons with

which to engage helicopters and fixed wing aircraft deserve brief special mention.
The difficulty here is to provide a weapon system that has a worthwhile chance
of actually hitting the target. There are two very basic approaches. One either
provides a sophisticated fire control system for a gun of adequate range or one
provides an unsophisticated control system relying extensively on the gunner who
with tons of ammunition can produce a cone of fire into which the target may fly. In
either case space, weight and costs will combine in IAVs to limit effectiveness.
The engagement of aircraft is a very complex business, calling for specialist
weapons. The infantry understandably demand anti-aircraft protection, but it
is best provided by those specialist weapons.

Firepower has several components which are summarised at Fig. 9.17. These components can each be associated with one or other of the factors in the familiar firepower equation expanded here to include the probability of firing.

$$P_{kill} = P_{firing} \times P_{reliability} \times P_{hit} \times P_{kill\ given\ a\ hit}$$

$-P_{kill\ given\ a\ hit}$	=	Lethality
$-P_{hit}$	=	Accuracy, Rate of fire, Fusing
$-P_{reliability}$	=	System reliability
$-P_{firing}$	=	Fire control, Application of fire, Training

Fig. 9.17 Components of firepower

The conflicts in role that emerge when one mounts a weapon of any sort on a IAV
have already been discussed. The infantry would be well advised not to overlook
these conflicts when stating its requirements for firepower in its armoured vehicles.

THE INTERRELATIONSHIPS BETWEEN THE BASIC
CHARACTERISTICS

That the basic characteristics are intimately related cannot be overemphasised.
These interrelationships occur in two distinct but obviously related contexts, the
mechanical and the human. Figure 9.18 depicts these relationships in the physical
context. Figure 9.19 depicts them in the human context.

The ultimate constraint in every case is cost, about which one need say no more.

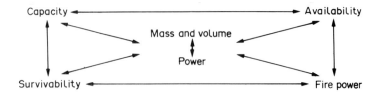

Fig. 9.18 Relationship of the basic characteristics
in the physical context.

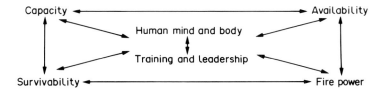

Fig. 9.19 Relation of the basic characteristics
in the human context

CONCLUSIONS

There are two quite fundamental conclusions that one can draw from this review
of infantry armoured vehicles, their development and basic characteristics.

The first is that designing and producing these vehicles does not pose the same
degree of technical challenge as designing and producing an effective and economic
main battle tank. The converse is that any nation that has the industrial capacity
to produce tanks can also produce infantry armoured vehicles. Indeed several
countries that do not produce tanks do produce infantry armoured vehicles of one
sort or another; a good example of this is Eire.

The other basic conclusion is that while the design and production of these vehicles
does not present the technical challenge associated with tanks, deciding the balance
of their conflicting roles is a considerable challenge. This is somewhat ironic in
the historical sense in that the debates of the interwar years and the experience
of the Second World War have permitted a very fine definition of what the main
battle tank must do. There is no such agreement in the context of infantry armoured
vehicles. The main reason is that the roles of a tank are more defined. The roles
of an infantry armoured vehicle are not easily balanced. Specialisation appears
to be the only way to resolve this difficulty.

The challenge of the future will be to refine the roles of these more specialised
vehicles in such a way that the costs of the required array of vehicles can be
borne and the vehicles themselves are proved to perform their roles adequately.

SELF TEST QUESTIONS

QUESTION 1   Why are terms such as armoured personnel carrier and mechanised
              infantry combat vehicle somewhat obscuring and misleading?

              Answer   ....

                          ....

                          ....

                          ....

                          ....

                          ....

QUESTION 2   What are the four basic characteristics of IAVs?

              Answer   ....

                          ....

                          ....

QUESTION 3   What is the essential difference between the tactical functions of
              mechanised infantry and armoured infantry?

              Answer   ....

                          ....

                          ....

                          ....

                          ....

                          ....

QUESTION 4   Why can it be said that in the history of AFVs the direct fire sup-
              port (DFS) vehicle was developed before the main battle tank (MBT)?

              Answer   ....

                          ....

                          ....

                          ....

                          ....

QUESTION 5   From the point of view of the infantry what is the technical significance
              of the Israeli Merkava tank?

              Answer   ....

                        ....

                        ....

                        ....

QUESTION 6   Why do you think the three types of infantry each may require a
              different set of variants?

              Answer   ....

                        ....

                        ....

                        ....

                        ....

                        ....

                        ....

                        ....

                        ....

                        ....

QUESTION 7   The DFS vehicle is a fundamental requirement of infantry in
              battle. Why is it that there are very few varieties of this vehicle
              available today?

              Answer   ....

                        ....

                        ....

                        ....

                        ....

                        ....

                        ....

QUESTION 8   Why are the terms "availability" and "survivability" coming to be
              preferred over the more conventional "mobility" and "protection"?

              Answer   ....

                        ....

                        ....

                        ....

                        ....

                        ....

QUESTION 9   Why does the configuration in which the infantrymen in the back of
              an IAV face inward tend to reduce the number of variants available?

              Answer   ....

                        ....

                        ....

                        ....

QUESTION 10   What are the tactical consequences of mounting an anti-APC cannon
              on an APC?

              Answer   ....

                        ....

                        ....

                        ....

                        ....

Answers on page 227.

10. Military Bridging

TERRAIN

The latticework of roads and tracks over most of Western Europe is so well developed that any new motorway cuts the existing routes at the rate of two or three per kilometre. Drainage ditches, streams and occasional larger rivers are all crossed, providing a firm smooth highway across soft meadows and through woodlands. Mobility is only really a problem to farmers, civil engineers and soldiers.

In military operations the main roads provide natural axes for attacking forces and would undoubtedly attract much traffic during war, but the sheer certainty that they will be used makes them priority targets for demolition and denial by the defender, and any traffic on them will be an obvious target for artillery and air attack. So while roads will be used by both sides out of contact with the enemy, the need for flexibility, concealment, surprise and good fire positions dictates that all but the lowest mobility vehicles should be able to take to the fields, hills and woods if they are to survive and be effective in battle.

Whilst mobility over rough terrain has high priority in vehicle design, there is a clear limit to the size and shape of gap that can be crossed without the aid of some sort of bridge. A wheeled combat vehicle will seldom be able to negotiate a ditch more than a metre wide and will have to find a way round, while ditches 3 metres wide are usually effective tank obstacles.

Terrain studies of North West Europe generally agree that the distribution of gaps greater than a metre wide is as indicated by Fig. 10.1. Some 70% of all gaps are less than 5 metres wide.

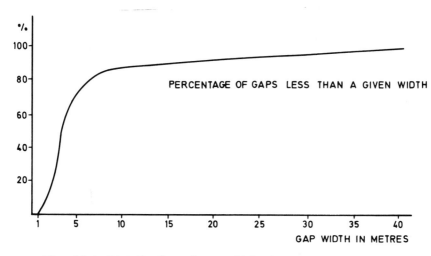

Fig. 10.1 Distribution of gap widths in North West Europe

Clearly there is a need for many short gap crossing devices and a reasonable range of medium span bridges. There are remarkably few wide rivers and canals.

MILITARY BRIDGING

Roles

Bridges will be needed for a variety of combat situations both in and out of
contact with the enemy. Some will have to be built under fire while others will
not be so urgent and can be constructed after the battle has moved on. Military
bridging is therefore conveniently divided into three categories to match the various
combat roles:

—   Close support bridging is designed to be laid rapidly under fire. In the past
     this was known as Assault bridging.

—   Deliberate support bridging is designed to provide crossings in other battle
     situations including unobserved artillery fire. It is subdivided into Dry and
     Wet support bridging. Dry support bridges span gaps freely from bank to
     bank or between piers, while wet support bridges use floating pontoons to
     provide either a continuous flexible deck or a series of short spans between
     buoyancy units.

—   Line of communication bridging is required for use in rear areas where speed
     of construction is not so important and continuous heavy loading is expected.
     In such situations peacetime construction methods would take months rather
     than hours, so obsolete military equipment bridging is normally used to pro-
     vide the necessary speed of response.

Military Load Classification

A term which needs explanation is Load class. Obviously there is a safe limit to
the load which any particular bridge can carry and there is a NATO standard
system for numbering both bridges and all types of military vehicles to ensure
that bridges are not overstressed. The load class of the bridge is boldly displayed at both ends on a yellow circular sign and vehicles may only cross the bridge
if their load class is less than or equal to that of the bridge. Normal convoy speeds
are assumed with spacings of 30.5 metres between vehicles. Examples of the forces
and dimensions which must be considered when classifying tanks or trucks are
given for two hypothetical cases in Fig. 10.2.

To give some real examples the Chieftain Mark 5 is Load Class 60, CVR(T) Scorpion
is Load Class 10, a fully laden 4-tonne truck is Load Class 12 and a 1/4 or 3/4
tonne Rover is Load Class 4.

The classification of the bridges analyses their ability to withstand the dynamic
loadings imposed by traffic and the calculations include strength in bending, shear
and torsion. Permanent civil bridges can be given a fixed classification, whereas
military equipment bridges have specified load classes for each span and configuration.

Reconnaissance

A bridge builder must have adequate knowledge of a proposed bridge site before
construction can be planned in detail. Even in the simplest cases the length of
the gap, the best position and alignment for the bridge and the ground conditions
are fundamental information. When deliberate support bridges are required the
reconnaissance must include details of suitable harbour areas, approach routes,
construction sites, essential earthworks, quantities of trackway and other stores
and information on river characteristics. It is important to appreciate this because
quoted bridge construction timings do not include the reconnaissance and planning
phases. Even placing a close support bridge in the heat of a battle calls for some
prior information or verbal report on the span and site conditions.

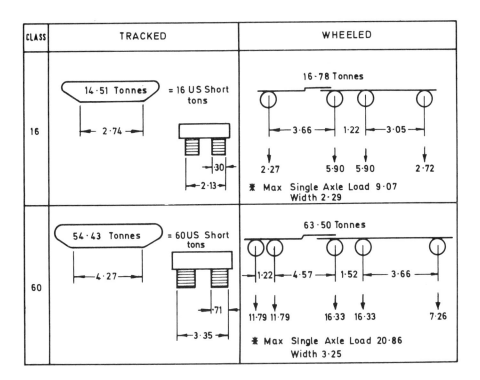

CLASS	TRACKED	WHEELED

*Axle loads may vary according to wheeled vehicle tyre pressures.

Loading in tonnes   Lengths in metres

Fig. 10.2 Military load classification – hypothetical examples of the maximum loading on Class 16 and Class 60 bridges.

CLOSE SUPPORT

Bridges for use in close contact with the enemy have to match the most demanding specification. They should be placed in less than 5 minutes, ideally 3, and must be of adequate strength to take main battle tanks. They must be laid with minimum exposure of the crew, be transported on a chassis able to keep up with the vehicles they are supporting and be laid, crossed and then lifted by the carrying vehicle so as to be ready for rapid re-use.

Length

A tricky decision is the choice of bridge length for close support bridges. It would be possible to devise a rapidly laid bridge of short span, for example 6 metres, which would suit a high percentage of situations. Indeed the most frequent and immediate demands of combat teams arise from ditches which sometimes do not even appear on the map. Another way to overcome this type of obstacle is by a proportion of combat vehicles carrying their own ditch-filling devices such as fascines. In spite of this the current solution adopted by most nations is to over–

insure by engineers carrying the longer spans to give more tactical flexibility.

Fascines

Although trials have been done using a variety of short gap crossing devices few
have proved to be acceptable encumbrances for fighting vehicles. The chestnut
paling fascine was too bulky and heavy for light armoured fighting vehicles, inflat-
able devices seem attractive, but durability, battle worthiness and expense mitigate
against present designs, while the most practical idea is to make fascines of light
plastic pipes. These have the major advantages of durability, cheapness and the
ability to take up the shape of a gap without blocking the flow of water. They
can be recovered in good condition for re-use, and a number of fascines of smaller
diameter can be used cumulatively to give the same effect as a larger one. Figure
10.3 illustrates the pipe fascine system.

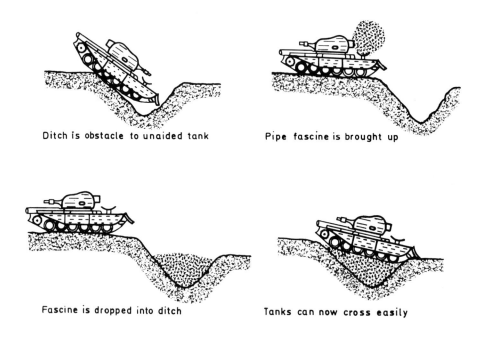

Fig. 10.3 Pipe fascine system

Tank Mounted Bridges

Close support bridges giving the longer spans have to be mounted on tank hulls
to meet the mobility standards and to provide the necessary crew protection. There
are two common methods of mounting and launching a tank mounted bridge. The
more popular system is illustrated by the British Chieftain No. 8 armoured vehicle
launch bridge (AVLB). The bridge is folded in half during carriage and the launch
is hydraulically controlled, opening the structure in a scissors fashion as shown
in Fig. 10.4.

The No. 8 AVLB provides a 23-metre span at Load Class 60 and the 18-tonne marag-
ing steel structure can be launched in about 3 minutes. There is also a No. 9
AVLB as part of the set associated with each launcher, and this is placed in an

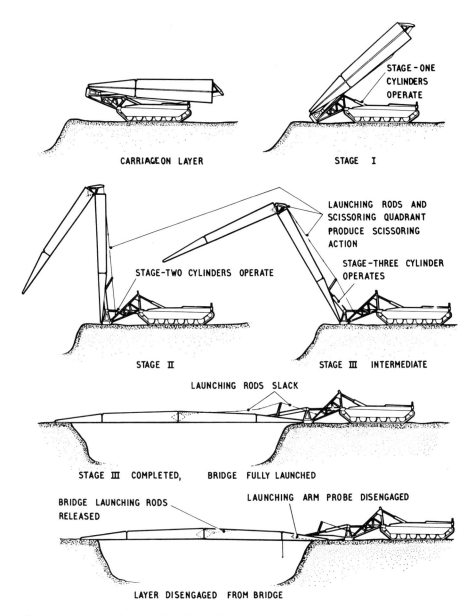

Fig. 10.4 The launching of Chieftain No. 8 armoured vehicle launch bridge

up-and-over mode using the same vehicle attachments. Other examples of tank-mounted scissors bridges in service are the Czechoslovak MT55 spanning 16 metres, the American M60 AVLB spanning 18 metres, and the French AMX30 spanning 20 metres.

The alternative launching system is used by the Russians in their MTU 20 bridge mounted on a T 55 tank chassis. While this bridge only gives a span of 18 metres at Load Class 50 it avoids one significant tactical disadvantage of the scissors system which is the height of the structure at the mid-point in the launch sequence.

Assault crossings being made in the forward area will be attractive enough targets
without drawing extra attention to themselves by waving bridges high in the air!
The MTU 20 is launched horizontally in cantilever fashion, extra length being
achieved by having ends which fold down to form a rigid part of the structure
(see Fig. 10.5a).

The German Brukenlegepanzer Biber is also launched horizontally. For carriage
it is mounted in two halves on its Leopard 2 chassis and in this case the top half
is slid forward, connected to the bottom half and the whole is then cantilevered
across gaps of up to 20 metres (see Fig. 10.5b).

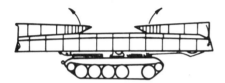

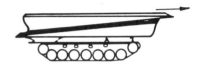

Fig. 10.5a The Russian MTU20   Fig. 10.5b The German Biber
            cantilever launched   cantilever launched
            close support bridge   close support bridge

In assault situations where gaps greater than close support bridge lengths are
met it is possible to lay bridges in tandem, making use of existing piers or even
barges as stepping stones. It is also possible to place one bridge down into the
gap and use it as a ramp from which to launch a second bridge (see Fig. 10.6).

The cost of tank-mounted close support bridges is likely to be very high, since
in addition to the loads they must carry they have also to be able to accommodate
considerable twist and crossfall and have a measure of resistance to shell fragments.

Fig. 10.6 No. 8 AVLBs being used in tandem

Bridge-laying tanks cost almost as much as gun tanks, so the common sense balance allows only a small scaling of the former.

DELIBERATE DRY SUPPORT BRIDGING

The limited number of close support bridges available leads to a demand for their replacement by longer term structures as early as possible so that they can be re-used. Although British close support bridges span up to 23 metres it is desirable that deliberate dry support bridges should give a free span of at least 30 metres at Load Class 70 to enable the majority of small rivers and canals to be bridged from firm bank seats.

The criteria used at the beginning of the Second World War for the design of the Bailey bridge are still valid today and explain why such old equipment is still so widely used throughout the world by contractors for temporary bridging projects. The components must be easily handled, readily carried on standard logistic transport, provide sufficient flexibility in design to give a variety of spans and load classes and it must be capable of being built by trained soldiers who need not be specialists in the equipment. Once a bridge is built the subsequent maintenance must be small.

The most significant change over the 40 years since Bailey was introduced is in the expected pace of the battle. Whereas a whole night used to be allocated for the construction of a 30-metre Class 60 Bailey bridge the timings were reduced to 3-4 hours by the 1970s, and the requirement for the 1980s is for a construction time of less than an hour. The means of surveillance and target acquisition have improved so much in the past two decades that it is no longer practical to expect extended periods of bridge construction to go undetected by the enemy. Another feature of the postwar years was the trend towards heavier tanks characterised by Conquerer which was Load Class 70. A big brother to Bailey was introduced to cope with the increased loads and this was the Heavy girder bridge which needed a crane for construction and so lost some of the flexibility of its predecessor (see Fig. 10.7). With the Challenger at Load Class 70 similar problems have been avoided by the use of new materials.

Medium Girder Bridge

The Heavy girder bridge was too heavy and too slow and so was fairly quickly relegated by the British to the line of communications role to be replaced by the current deliberate dry support bridge Medium girder bridge (MGB). This is manufactured in a light zinc/magnesium/aluminium alloy with panels, each an easy four-man lift, which pin together to form the main girders. The heaviest items are only a six-man load (245 kg) and a 30-metre Class 60 bridge can be built in less than 2 hours under ideal conditions and 3-4 hours operationally. Class 70 loads can be carried with a slight reduction in span. Training is of course important and as with all equipment bridges, planning, teamwork and good site preparation are the key to rapid builds. Although the bridge can accommodate crossfall and bank seat differences of up to 1:10, these can add considerably to construction problems and timings. The bridge can be built with either shallow girders using the box-shaped panels alone for short spans and light loads, or for tank crossings of spans over 9 metres the box girders are reinforced by incorporating bottom panels, thereby deepening and strengthening them. The top panels and the A-shaped panels can be seen clearly in Fig. 10.8.

The bridge is assembled on rollers carefully positioned on the home bank and the launching process employs a simple cantilever arrangement pushing a light launching

Fig. 10.7 Heavy girder bridge under construction

nose across the gap and balancing this by the main weight of the bridge itself.
The launching nose has to be a little longer than half the gap width and once it
touches down on rollers on the far bank the remainder of the bridge can be pushed
forward into its final position either using a vehicle or by hand. The launching
nose is then stripped, the rollers removed and ramps, kerbs and decking rapidly
placed in position. The launching process is illustrated in Fig. 10.9. Recovery
and stripping of an MGB is equally simple and employs the same processes in
reverse.

It is interesting to see the enormous improvements achieved by the designers of

Fig. 10.8 Medium girder bridge. Double storey
configuration giving 30 metres at Load Class 60

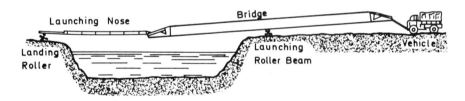

Fig. 10.9 Medium girder bridge during the launching process

MGB in comparison with Bailey. These have been made possible by taking advantage
of new alloys and combining these with some ingenious time-saving devices (see
Fig. 10.10). There is now little scope for further improvement with current
materials without resorting to some form of mechanical assistance.

The free span of an MGB at Class 60 is restricted to 30 metres, which is adequate
for most circumstances, but greater spans can be achieved in two ways using special
additional equipment. One method is by the use of piers and the other by increasing the strength of the bridge in bending.

The span junction set has been designed to enable bridges to be launched over
existing or improvised piers, leaving a pinned joint at the support. Such articulation also allows the bridge to be used in conjunction with floating piers. A portable
pier set for an MGB has been introduced and added to the bridge configurations
available. This is illustrated at Fig. 10.11.

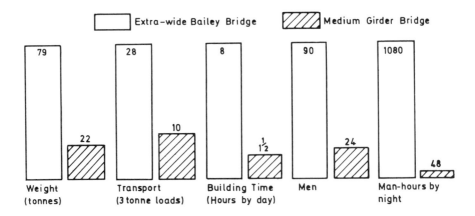

Fig. 10.10   Comparison between extra wide Bailey bridge and MGB
for 30-metre span at Class 60

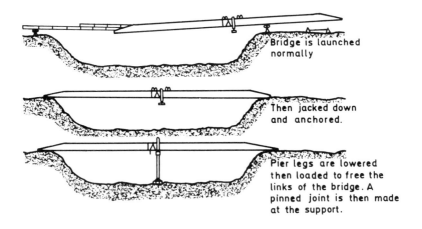

Fig. 10.11 Installing a two-span MGB and pier

Piers can sometimes be adapted from the remains of a demolished structure, otherwise temporary piers require firm footings if they are to carry heavy loads. In
the case of floating piers adequate buoyancy is essential and fairly constant water
levels desirable. There are, therefore, occasions when piers are not the best
answer.

A simple method of increasing the bending strength and thereby the free span
attainable with the MGB is effectively to deepen the beams by the attachment of
a link-reinforcing set. This is shown in Fig. 10.12 and increases the Class 60
free span from 30 to 50 metres. Readers acquainted with basic structural principles
will understand the merit of providing an underslung tensile member of this sort,
but there are some practical difficulties in fitting it, additional construction time
is also necessary, and in some circumstances the link reinforcement may be hanging
in the water, which is certainly not desirable. Nevertheless, it is yet another
demonstration of the flexibility of the MGB.

Fig. 10.12 The MGB link reinforcement is painted white in the photograph

Mechanical Assistance

Rapid construction times can be achieved quite easily if the use of mechanical
aids and specialist vehicles is regarded as acceptable. The Soviet TMM truck-
mounted scissors bridge, for example, provides 10 metres of bridge per vehicle
and can be laid in a matter of minutes per truck, each adding another section to
the bridge. It is illustrated at Fig. 10.13.

Future Systems

The next generation of British deliberate dry support bridging is required to
achieve even swifter construction times of 30 minutes using only a section of ten
men. It follows that there must be heavy dependence on a launching vehicle together
with lifting aids for the heavier sections of the bridge. Options range from a
sophisticated hydraulic system mounted on a high mobility chassis akin to AVLB
in both appearance and cost, to a truck-mounted launch rail upon which sections
of bridge can be hung, assembled and launched across a gap rather like drawing
a curtain. The purse holders naturally prefer the cheaper end of the scale.

Fig. 10.13 The TMM truck-mounted scissors bridge

WET SUPPORT BRIDGING

The deliberate wet support bridging begins to come into its own for wet gaps of over 30 metres, that is when piers would be necessary for dry support bridges. Floating bridges can only be used to cross water obstacles into which pontoons can be launched and upon which they can be expected to float without damage. Sites with steep high banks or shallow turbulent water are obviously not well suited for pontoons, although with time and effort some of the ramp and launching problems can be overcome (see Fig. 10.14).

In addition to the practical restrictions on its use, wet support bridging has a number of characteristics which can be serious military disadvantages. Because they must float, pontoons or other buoyancy arrangements are prone to damage in battle which would make them leak and sink. They tend to be cumbersome, costly to produce and require much maintenance. Construction is manpower intensive, and

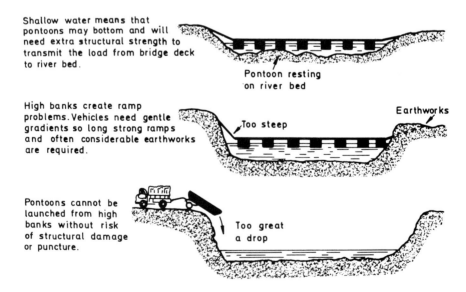

Fig. 10.14 Ramp and launching problems

when in the water pontoons must either have their own power or tugs must be available to place them in the bridge. Even after construction a floating bridge will need to be manned to check on couplings, anchorages and, particularly in tidal rivers, to adjust the length of the bridge by the insertion or removal of pontoons. Engineers maintaining the temporary Bailey pontoon bridge for the main line of communication south of Mandalay in the Burma Campaign had to cope with a 10-metre rise in water level. Extra sections of bridge were constantly having to be added to make a maximum length of 280 metres. One can imagine the supervision and maintenance needed to keep that structure open. In spite of all those snags the floating bridge has a flexibility attested to by military history throughout the ages when rapid crossings of major water obstacles have been called for. Most recently the Egyptians used pontoon bridges to cross the Suez Canal in the 1973 Yom Kippur War.

The two examples of deliberate wet support bridges in Fig. 10.15 illustrate the design options.

Buoyancy can be provided continuously under a flexible deck by closely coupling pontoons. Alternatively, pontoons can be used more like stepping stones with rigid spans pinned between them.

As with deliberate dry support bridging the construction times demanded for deliberate wet support bridging to meet tactical requirements and to reduce the risks of detection and destruction have been steadily reduced over the last three

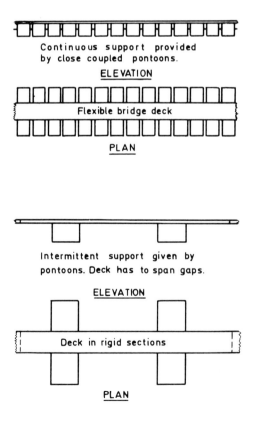

Continuous support provided
by close coupled pontoons.

ELEVATION

Flexible bridge deck

PLAN

Intermittent support given by
pontoons. Deck has to span gaps.

ELEVATION

Deck in rigid sections

PLAN

Fig. 10.15 Design options for deliberate wet support bridges

decades. Timings in the order of 100 metres in 30 minutes are sought, and the possible solutions fall into three categories.

The first is the floating version of the deliberate dry support bridge. In the case of the British this is the Floating MGB. The advantages of using many standard parts and drills tend to be outweighed by the high manpower needed and the call for numerous tugs, as the buoyancy pontoons designed for the bridge have no power. MGB pontoons are simple, comparatively cheap and easily launched (see Fig. 10.16). The Floating MGB takes an hour to build across a 100-metre gap in ideal conditions and so does not really match up to the requirement.

Fig. 10.16 MGB pontoons being launched

The second category of deliberate wet support bridge is the Soviet choice, PMP, a version of which has also been adopted by the Americans under the name Ribbon bridge. The pontoons are carried on vehicles, folded and ready for launching. Once in the water they automatically unfold and are close coupled with the aid of tugs. Construction timings are considerably better than Floating MGB. The PMP is illustrated in Fig. 10.17. The equipment is relatively cheap and durable.

The third alternative is the Amphibious bridge, an expensive solution but one which matches the operational concept of rapid construction and dispersal as well as the specified timings. The French pioneered this equipment with their Gillois, and subsequently the German version M2 was purchased by the British. The USA has a similar Mobile amphibious bridge. As the name implies, the bridge is in the form of large amphibious vehicles, or rigs, which have powerful marine engines and link rapidly side by side to form a bridge (as illustrated in Fig. 10.18).

Fig. 10.17 A PMP pontoon being launched

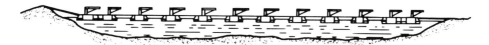

Fig. 10.18 M2 rigs linked up side by side to form a 10.4-m Class 60
bridge for wheels and tracks

M2 rigs are soft skinned, 11 metres long, 3.5 metres wide and weigh 22 tonnes.
Each forms 8 metres of bridge or they can be close coupled to form ferries
(see Fig. 10.19).

M2 rigs have a crew of four, and there is no requirement for any outside help when
forming the bridge because each rig has its own crane arm for lifting deck units
and the motors are run continuously to hold the bridge in position to obviate
anchorages. Considerable skill and much training is needed to use this type of
equipment to full advantage, and it is considered necessary to have specialists
to man it.

Ferries

Ferries rightly fall under the same heading as deliberate wet support bridging.
Certainly Floating MGB, PMP and Amphibious bridges can all be constructed as
ferries or rafts. Amphibious bridges are the most successful in the role as their
propulsion is so much more powerful, which makes the ferry easier to control.
The Soviet GSP and the British Heavy ferry are, on the other hand, specifically

Fig. 10.19 Three M2 rigs close coupled to form a Class 60 ferry

designed for use solely as ferries. From the point of view of the customer, bridges are far more desirable because they can pass a continuous flow of traffic over a water obstacle, whereas ferries are painfully slow by comparison. Bridges are, of course, much easier targets for the enemy. Like all deliberate wet support bridges ferries are tied to operating between suitable access points for vehicles on either bank.

OTHER ASPECTS OF BRIDGING

Swimming and Snorkelling

Although not strictly part of bridging, the alternatives to combat bridging should be mentioned in this chapter. Some nations, notably the Soviets, have a policy of making all their combat vehicles capable of either swimming or snorkelling. This is tactically very attractive, as it increases battlefield mobility and so adds greatly to the flexibility of movement without recourse to engineer support. A look back at Fig. 10.1 will remind readers that the majority of gaps in North West Europe are little more than ditches, and the shape of these is much more important than the amount of water they contain. This is well illustrated by Fig. 10.20 which shows the British high mobility load carrier Stalwart stuck firmly in a ditch in spite of its amphibious capability and cross-country performance.

In order to provide a swimming capability a combat vehicle must be as light as possible, and this is hardly compatible with the need for protection against enemy weapons. The more protection given means a greater volume of water must be displaced to support the vehicle. The Soviet BMP can swim, but provides very little protection as the penalty for its excellent mobility and flotation, whereas

Fig. 10.20 Stalwart in trouble in a ditch

the British FV432 is much better protected but only floats with the aid of fragile
screens whch are erected when needed. Swimming by combat vehicles requires
a skilled crew, good entry and exit points and a current slow enough to be overcome by the thrust of the vehicle's propulsion. Yet one more problem is posed
to swimming vehicles by canals which in Germany are normally revetted by steel
sheet piling. This makes entry into the water very tricky and climbing out impossible without plant or explosives to break down the piling. For all these reasons
the current British policy is not to require an amphibious capability in the design
of their next generation of armoured fighting vehicles, except for an engineer
pathfinder.

Snorkelling is resorted to when a vehicle is too heavy to float, and this technique
enables heavily armoured tanks to cross rivers of up to 5 metres deep provided
the tank can enter the river, which must have a firm bottom, and also provided
that when it reaches the far bank it is able to climb out and fight. These restrictions clearly limit the opportunities for the employment of snorkels, and the
technique is not favoured by the British although practised extensively by the
Warsaw Pact countries.

Site Preparation

Reconnaissance will reveal the feasibility of a bridge site, and as important as
the obstacle itself are the approaches, entry and exit points and construction
areas. Gradients will have to be reduced using engineer plant, and trackway
will be needed to prevent vehicles bogging in. The most convenient but also
expensive trackway is illustrated in Fig. 10.21 and is available in Class 30 and
Class 60. It can be laid in seconds from a combat engineer tractor (CET) or a
4-tonne truck with a special mounting.

Fig. 10.21 Class 60 trackway mounted on combat engineer tractor

The CET is the British Army's armoured pathfinder vehicle. It can swim power-
fully (see Fig. 10.22), and has a rocket projected self-righting anchor to assist
it in climbing out of the more difficult rivers; it has a high digging output. As
well as preparing the home bank, it can cross an obstacle independently to work
on the far bank, so reducing the delays once the bridge is completed.

Air-portable bridges

For short spans and lower load classes likely to be required in an air-portable
operation there is a need for a structure which can be easily erected by hand
and providing maximum versatility. The Class 16 Air-portable bridge fills this
role with a 15-metre clear span at Class 16 or a floating bridge configuration
also suitable for ferrying. Any set of equipment meeting such varied roles is
liable to suffer from snags because so much is demanded from it. The Air-portable
bridge is no exception, but serves to meet the limited needs in this field.

Small bridges can, of course, be placed in position by helicopter in some situations,
but the vulnerability of the aircraft reduces the attractiveness of such use in
the forward area.

Improvised Bridges

It would be wrong to think that military equipment bridges are the only answer
to obstacle crossing. While they undoubtedly provide essential speed and con-
venience and do away with the need for individual designs, there will be times

Fig. 10.22 Combat engineer tractor swimming

when the right equipment will not be available and the rapid patching of a partially demolished structure will be the best or the only immediate solution. Engineers
should always keep their eyes open for local resources such as supplies of hard-
core, steel beams, timber and, of course, any plant which could be usefully com-
mandeered. Look at any builders yard. You never know when the contents might
come in useful!

LINE OF COMMUNICATION BRIDGES

It has been mentioned earlier that the short-term solution for line of communication
bridging is to use obsolete deliberate dry support bridging equipment. This can
be quickly and easily constructed and needs less maintenance than wet support
bridging. It can also more readily be adapted for rail communications which will
undoubtedly suffer in any war. The Russians have a variety of bridges specially
designed for the line of communications role to support major forward movement
of logistic support.

CONCLUSIONS

Military bridging in the combat area requires the intelligent and educated use
of specially designed equipment and machines to form a standard design bridge
very rapidly to match the gap size and load class demanded to meet the commander's
plans. Reconnaissance and detailed planning are fundamental to the success of
a bridging operation, and training and teamwork are the keys to fast construction
times. There is plenty of scope for initiative, ingenuity and boldness when in

contact with the enemy, while the longer-term solutions are likely to require greater civil engineering knowledge and skill and will depend more on local resources.

In the course of the Second World War campaign from the Normandy landings to the arrival of the British forces in Berlin, Royal Engineers of 21 Army Group constructed 29 miles of Bailey bridge, 3 miles of Floating Bailey and 3 miles of Folding boat equipment bridge. Since then all our equipment, like that of both allies and potential enemies, has improved enormously, while concepts of operations have responded to many swings of political and military policy, but the ground over which battles have to be fought and therefore the bridging·challenge has altered little.

SELF TEST QUESTIONS

QUESTION 1   What length of bridge would be needed to span 70% of all the gaps
              in North West Europe?

              Answer   ....

QUESTION 2   Why are bridges and vehicles given a load class and what is the
              load class of the Chieftain Mark 5 tank?

              Answer   ....

              ....

QUESTION 3   What are the three main categories of military bridging and what
              are the approximate time scales for construction.

              Answer   ....

              ....

              ....

QUESTION 4   What were the main criteria used for the design of the Bailey bridge
              at the beginning of the Second World War.

              Answer   ....

              ....

              ....

              ....

              ....

QUESTION 5   How can close support bridges be combined to give crossings
              greater than their individual spans?

              Answer   ....

              ....

QUESTION 6   How can deliberate dry support bridges be adapted to cross gaps
              greater than 30 metres?

              Answer   ....

              ....

QUESTION 7   There are numerous disadvantages of deliberate wet support bridges,
              but what major advantages do floating bridges have over other
              types?

              Answer   ....

              ....

              ....

QUESTION 8   What is the single most important disadvantage of using ferries
                as opposed to deliberate wet support bridges?

                Answer   ....

QUESTION 9   What is the current UK policy on armoured fighting vehicles
                swimming?

                Answer   ....

QUESTION 10   What are the alternatives open for line of communications bridges
                assuming no assault or up-to-date support bridges are available?

                Answer   ....

                          ....

                          ....

Answers on page 228.

Answers to Self Test Questions

CHAPTER 1

Page 17

QUESTION 1   The introduction of the machine gun which pinned the infantry to a trench system and prevented the use of cavalry combined with the quagmire conditions of the battlefield which restricted movement.

QUESTION 2   A rhomboidal shape gave the tank very good cross-country performance but restricted fire from sponsons on the side of the hull.

QUESTION 3   The Christie tank was able to run on either its tracks or wheels. The suspension system was also an innovation.

QUESTION 4   The very light tank (infantry weapon carrier).
The fast light tank (reconnaissance vehicle).
The medium tank (exploitation tank).
The infantry tank (heavily protected).

QUESTION 5   a.   The Cruiser tank.
b.   The infantry tank.

QUESTOIN 6   In no particular order:

Firepower.
Protection.
Mobility.

QUESTION 7   Any four from:

Communication, Surveillance, Silence, Maintainability, Endurance and probably the two major additional factors today, Cost and Reliability.

QUESTION 8   a.   It allows them to accept a limited gun depression.
b.   It gives them greater freedom in their stowage arrangements for ammunition, etc.

QUESTION 9   The Israelis believe in shock action but also in the need to survive the initial onslaught when they may be greatly outnumbered.

QUESTION 10   The General Abrams tank is the first production tank to have a gas turbine engine and it also has composite armour.

CHAPTER 2

Page 38

QUESTION 1   The main role is "shock action" and the destruction of enemy armour.
              Other subsidiary roles are the destruction of light and unarmoured
              vehicles, men in the open and fortified areas.

QUESTION 2   Short range   0 – 1000 m
              Medium range   1000 – 2000 m
              Long range   2000 – 4000 m

QUESTION 3   a.   "M" kill – Mobility kill.
              b.   "F" kill – Firepower kill.
              c.   "K" kill – "Knocked out".
              d.   "P" kill – Personnel kill (usually applied to MICVs).

QUESTION 4   a.   Kinetic energy attack.
              b.   Hollow charge warhead (HEAT).
              c.   High explosive squash head (HESH).

QUESTION 5   HESH is most useful as a multi-purpose round, capable of attack-
              ing AFVs and other targets.

QUESTION 6   a.   Production maintenance and setting up errors.
              b.   Correction of the moment.
              c.   Range determination.
              d.   Gunners errors.
              e.   Residual inherent errors.

QUESTION 7   a.   Visual range estimation.
              b.   Correction of fall shot.
              c.   Optical methods.
              d.   Sub-calibre ranging.
              e.   Laser range finding.

QUESTION 8   Trunnion tilt occurs then the trunnions are not level (e.g. tank
              side on to a hill) and causes misalignment of the sight and gun
              barrel.

QUESTION 9   In order to take on secondary targets that it would be uneconomical
              to engage with the main armament.

QUESTION 10   a.   Calculating and controlling the gun lay.
              b.   Input/output monitoring.
              c.   Confidence checks.
              d.   Fault diagnosis.
              e.   Ability ot accept manual inputs.

CHAPTER 3

Page 53

QUESTION 1   The need to move it by rail and/or by road, and in particular the
              Continental rail gauges.

QUESTION 2   A high-velocity gun will mean a long heavy gun with large buffers and recuperators, a long recoiling length and larger ammunition to stow.

QUESTION 3   It is important to achieve maximum depression in order to engage targets without being unnecessarily exposed. This is particularly important on reverse slope positions.

QUESTION 4   The mantlet allows the gun to elevate and depress whilst protecting the turret interior. Mantlets are generally "interior" or "exterior".

QUESTION 5   The rotary base junction provides an interface between the hull and the turret for all electrical and hydraulic services.

QUESTION 6   A bustle helps to balance the turret and also provides additional space under armour in the turret.

QUESTION 7   The L/C ratio is the ratio between the length of track on the ground and the distance between the track centres and it is important because extremes in the ratio could make the vehicle difficult to steer.

QUESTION 8   Tactical height is the height is the height of the tank that has to be exposed in order to engage the enemy.

QUESTION 9   The height of the hull is determined by:

a.   The height of the power pack.
b.   Interior suspension systems.
c.   Vertically stowed ammunition.
d.   Height of a seated/reclining driver.

QUESTION 10 $$NGP = \frac{Vehicle\ weight}{Area\ of\ tracks\ in\ contact\ with\ the\ ground}$$

CHAPTER 4

Page 80

QUESTION 1   The up strokes, compression and exhaust would tend to blow the paper away; the answer must be induction or expansion. On induction, the inlet valve is open so no vacuum is generated at low speeds. On expansion, both valves are shut, the descending piston will generate a vacuum and the paper is sucked in.

QUESTION 2   Fuel-rich mixtures have low A/F, less than 15/1.

QUESTION 3   Chilling of the air charge by the cold hardware will be more pronounced in a small engine. The bigger engine is likely to start better.

QUESTION 4   On over-run with engine braking. So the engine is mechanically viable at high speeds, but needs a governor to prevent smoking if run too fast on load. Air/fuel mixing within the cylinder takes time in a CI so speed is restricted. SI engines run on premixed charge, combustion is fast and does not inhibit running speed.

QUESTION 5   Less than 25%. The turbocharger will raise the temperature of the charge as well as its pressure, so charge density will not increase by a factor of as much as 1.25.

QUESTION 6   Waste-gates are used to prevent over-boost at the top end of the engine speed range. In a CI, a similar effect can be achieved by restricting the amount of fuel injected per cycle at the higher speeds. But the mixture of a SI engine cannot be made significantly leaner, so turbine power and turbocharger speed cannot be controlled in this way.

QUESTION 7   Absolute nonsense. It is difficult enough to ensure a worthwhile excess of turbine work over compressor work in a gas turbine, and heating the air before the compressor will increase the compressor work needed to compress it. The engine would not even drive itself.

QUESTION 8   High-pressure ratio leads to large compressor temperature rise and large turbine temperature drop. The turbine exhaust will not be hot enough to heat the compressed air.

QUESTION 9   Rolling resistance   = 8% of 540 kN = 43.2 kN

Gradient resistance   = 540 kN × sin 8° = 75.2 kN

Road load   = 118.4 kN

Road power   = 1080 kN m/s

Road speed   = 9.12 m/s or 32.8 km/h

QUESTION 10   Road power   = 1080 kW (max)

Engine power   = 1080 kW ÷ 0.72

                         = 1500 kW

CI sfc   = 45 kg/h ÷ (1/4 × 500 kW)

                         = 0.36 kg/kW h

CI fuel   = (0.36 kg/kW h x 1500 kW x 1/4) x 10 h

                         = 1350 kg or 1607 litres

Turbine sfc   = 0.464 kg/kW h

Turbine fuel   = 1740 kg or 2351 litres

CHAPTER 5

Page 100

QUESTION 1   For engine power of 80% maximum:

Engine speed   = 62.7% (Fig. 4.4)

Engine speed range = 100/62.7

But vehicle makes 10 km/h maximum in LOW,

   Vehicle makes 10 km/h at 62.7% speed in SECOND.

   Maximum vehicle speed in second gear   =   15.9 km/h

QUESTION 2   Maximum vehicle speed in HIGH   =   80 km/h.

Using 100/62.7 engine speed range from above:

Maximum speed in SECOND   =   15.9 km/h.
Maximum speed in THIRD   =   25.4 km/h.
Maximum speed in FOURTH   =   40.6 km/h.
Maximum speed in FIFTH   =   64.8 km/h.
Maximum speed in SIXTH   =   103.3 km/h.

So: Vehicle needs SIX gears. Rather more than 85% power
      will then be available at worst.

QUESTION 3   For engine power of 80% maximum:

Engine speed   =   45% (Fig. 5.4)

Engine speed range   =   100/45

Maximum speeds in gears are:

10, 22.2, 49.4 and 109.7 km/h.

With a gas turbine FOUR gears are needed.

QUESTION 4   The top speed of the vehicle will increase considerably, (not quite
              50%), but it must retain low-speed manoeuvring ability. So its
              speed range is increased, and MORE gears should be provided.
              This is PART-ONLY offset by the fact that a lower percentage
              of power availability might become acceptable.

QUESTION 5   If the annulus were stationary, clockwise sun drive would give
              clockwise carrier movement. If the carrier were stationary, clock-
              wise sun drive would give anti-clockwise annulus movement. So
              by a logical extension, clockwise sun drive and anti-clockwise carrier
              drive will give even more anti-clockwise annulus movement.

QUESTION 6   Yes. Suppose annulus and carrier both to be driven clockwise at
              the same speed. Then the sun (output) would necessarily turn
              at the same speed too; the whole system would turn "solidly". Now
              let the annulus be stopped. The planets will have to turn in the
              carrier, anti-clockwise relative to the carrier. So their teeth at
              their inner (sun) radius will be advancing clockwise faster than
              the carrier itself, driving the sun faster than the carrier-overdrive.
              (If you find this hard to see in your mind – try drawing some
              sketches with arrows on them.)

QUESTION 7   The torque converter will be best; it can multiply torque and
              hence tractive effort, and can best stand slipping. The driver
              controlled clutch is next; the driver can pre-rev the engine
              before clutch engagement, to make most use of its flywheel effect
              to "jerk" the vehicle forward. The centrifugal clutch does not
              permit this.

QUESTION 8   Yes, It is intrinsically straight running when not being steered,
              whereas a differential can "wander" – down the road-camber,
              for instance.

QUESTION 9   Possibly, yes. If the steer is operated with the engine running
              in neutral forward gear, it may pivot steer, as one sun drives
              forward and the other backwards, the annuli being not driven and
              hence stationary. But inequality between the track to ground reac-
              tions on the two sides may upset this, causing the annuli to "drift"

round. Only if they are positively braked can we be sure of a
pivot turn.

QUESTION 10   Intrinsically, it steers the wrong way! (Opposite to the direction
of steer when going forward.) This oddity can be eliminated in
the control system.

CHAPTER 6

Page 133

QUESTION 1   a.   Penetrating lugs, preferably self-cleaning.
b.   Smooth, possibly with narrow circumferential grooves.
c.   Combination of bulk drainage channels and transverse pipes.

QUESTION 2   On a frictional soil the traction is proportional to vertical load
only; thus, being independent of contact area, both vehicles
will have the same grip.

QUESTION 3   Resistance to slew is due to the moment of the lateral forces on
the tracks (increasing with L); it is overcome by the couple
formed by the longitudinal forces (increasing with C). If this
is insufficient (due to L/C being too large) the vehicle will not
steer.

QUESTION 4   a.   Direct stress on bushes approximately halved.
b.   Maximum shear angle in bushes halved.
c.   Track splitting easier.
d.   Sprocket drive surfaces renewable.

QUESTION 5   Maximum acceleration   = $(2\pi f)^2\ H$

Hence we need $9.81 > 0.2\ (2\pi f)^2$

$$f\ =\ v/\lambda < 1.12\ \text{Hz}$$
$$v\ <\ 16.7\ \text{m/s}.$$

QUESTION 6

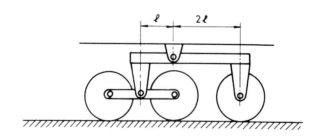

QUESTION 7   A torsion bar gives a linear rate; this must be kept as low as
possible so that the natural frequency is low (say < 2 Hz). With

bump travel limited by bar length, a sufficiently large bump force (say 5 × static) becomes impossible to achieve without the addition of a delayed action spring.

QUESTION 8   Figure 6.22 shows that, independent of damping, a ratio $f/f_n > \sqrt{2}$ is needed.

Hence $f_n = \dfrac{1}{2\pi} \sqrt{\dfrac{k}{m}} = \dfrac{1}{2\pi} \sqrt{\dfrac{300 \times 10^3}{5000}} = 1.23$ Hz

Hence we need $f = v/\lambda > 1.23 \sqrt{2}$ or 1.74 Hz.

$\lambda < 12/1.74$ or 6.88 m.

QUESTION 9   If we choose damping ratio $\zeta = 0.35$, then damping coefficient
$c = 2\zeta\sqrt{km} = 2 \times 0.35 \sqrt{300 \times 10^3 \times 5 \times 10^3}$
$= 27.1$ kN per m/s.

QUESTION 10   If we assume a supported mass of 75 kg on the seat, then

$$f_n = \dfrac{1}{2\pi} \sqrt{\dfrac{60 \times 10^3}{75}} = 4.5 \text{ Hz}.$$

This is undesirable since it will amplify disturbances in the region of this frequency which coincides with that of major biodynamic resonancies.

CHAPTER 7

Page 146

QUESTION 1   The most common material used to protect WWI tanks was boiler plate which was rivetted to a framework of angle iron.

QUESTION 2   Whittakers directional probability variation attempted to theoretically analyse the direction sof attack against a tank and hence how best to distribute the armour on a tank.

QUESTION 3   The disadvantages of thin hard steel plates are:

a.   They are difficult to fabricate and weld.
b.   They often fail catastrophically if overmatched.

QUESTION 4   Aluminium alloy armours are easy to fabricate and weld, provide inherent stiffness for vehicle manufacture, and tend to provide a vehicle which for a given level of protection is lighter than a similar steel vehicle.

QUESTION 5   Equivalent thickness is the length of the path the projectile need to travel through the armour plate if it struck the target horizontally

$$T_\beta = T_N \cos \beta.$$

QUESTION 6   The ideal armour material should be

a.   Effective.
b.   Lightweight.
c.   Cost effective.
d.   Amenable to modern construction methods.
e.   Low bulk.

QUESTION 7   The most common elements to be found in armour steel are:

                         Manganese
                         Nickel
                         Chrome
                         Molybdenum
                         Vanadium

QUESTION 8   Body armour tends to be heavy and reduces the mobility of the
              individual. Also, if the energy from the projectile is not dis-
              sipated then this energy may still be transferred to the body
              with equally fatal secondary results.

QUESTION 9   The three most common ceramics used as armour materials are:

                         Boron carbide
                         Silicon carbide
                         Alumina

QUESTION 10   Composite armour offers greatly enhanced protection against
              hollow charge and HESH attack without degradation of the pro-
              tection offered against KE attack.

              CHAPTER 8

              Page 168

QUESTION 1   The two prime tasks of the crew on the battlefield are to
              manoeuvre the vehicle and to fire the armament. Other sub-
              sidiary tasks are operating the radio, repositioning ammunition
              and servicing ancilliary equipment.

QUESTION 2   Because it was thought essential to provide an extra crew member
              to act as co-driver.

QUESTION 3   The functions of a four-man crew are:

                         Commander
                         Gunner
                         Loader/Radio operator
                         Driver

QUESTION 4   The most likely combinations of crew duties are:

                         Commander/Gunner
                         Commander/Loader
                         Commander/Driver

QUESTION 5   The particular advantage of a cleft turret design is that the gun
              can depress fully without the constraint of a turret roof.

QUESTION 6   The main reason why oscillating turrets are only suitable for light
              vehicles is that in order to provide the necessary level of pro-
              tection afforded to an MBT it would make the tank unacceptably
              heavy.

QUESTION 7   The major problems arise from the complexity required to keep
              the driver facing forward and the competition for all-round vision
              between the driver and the commander.

QUESTION 8   The major limitations for a forward engine design for an MBT are:

    a.   Providing sufficient gun depression.
    b.   Optical paths crossing engine/transmission compartments.
    c.   Balance of protection.

QUESTION 9   The major problem with any fixed gun design is the problem of firing on the move, particularly at targets acquired on the flanks.

QUESTION 10 An effective three man MBT would lead to a smaller tank which would offer better protection for the crew and would be more cost effective. The problem lies with making the tank as effective and flexible as the current four man concepts.

CHAPTER 9

Page 194

QUESTION 1   In any mechanised battalion there are several variants to the basic APC such as command, signals, ambulance, mortar, anti-tank and logistics vehicles whose number will almost equal that of the basic APCs. As all of these vehicles are commonly referred to APCs, the term obscures the existence of the variety of variants.

QUESTION 2   The four basic characteristics of IAVs are: capacity, protection or survivability, mobility or availability, and firepower.

QUESTION 3   Mechanised infantry normally fight from the ground moving from point to point on the battlefield supported by tanks and artillery by APC. Armoured infantry support armour by moving with them in MICVs, fighting from their vehicles whenever they can, and dismounting only when this is required in order to achieve local task.

QUESTION 4   The first tanks, e.g. the Mark V of the First World War, were effectively DFS vehicles. It was not until the Second World War that the concept of a main battle tank emerged, from the writings of Fuller, Liddel Hart and Guderian, and the experience of both the Allies and the Germans in the early years of the war.

QUESTION 5   The Israeli Merkava, while manifestly a tank, proves the technical feasibility of building a vehicle with the survivability, availability and firepower of a tank and the capacity of an APC.

QUESTION 6   Two basic factors determine the number of different variants produced. The number of sub-units who require the mobility, protection, firepower and capacity of IAVs to perform their tactical function and expense. In IS operations, most functions are conducted statically or are not performed at all. Thus mortars are normally statically deployed (and seldom used) and anti-tank weapons are seldom required at all. MICV are by far the most expensive IAV. When determining their requirement for variants, every effort is made to take advantage of existing variants of APCs. Thus APC variants tend to be the most numerous.

QUESTION 7   The basic reason is that any MBT can perform the tactical functions of a DFS vehicle, however at perhaps higher cost per vehicle. Many armies feel that since they must have tanks, it is cheaper in the long run to go for a single vehicle in larger numbers than take on the logistics, training and organisational complexity and expense of having two vehicles, one an MBT and the other a DFS vehicle.

QUESTION 8   The terms "protection" and "mobility" are not normally construed as including many of the factors that appear as inherent in "survivability" and "availability". As these additional factors become increasingly significant through the growth of technology, it seems appropriate to use the terms that include them.

QUESTION 9   Infantry face outward in order to be able to see through vision ports and to fire through firing ports as in BMP. Therefore, the walls must be kept clear of storage tanks and stowage racks which must be built in between the seats. This superstructure thus makes it difficult to arrange wide areas for other functions such as command posts or ambulances.

QUESTION 10   When an anti-APC cannon is mounted in an APC the platoon and company commander are presented with the dilemma: whether to site and use the vehicle as a weapon platform or as an APC. This dilemma is the direct result of the conflict that results because each role precludes the vehicles' being employed with maximum effectiveness in the other.

CHAPTER 10

Page 217

QUESTION 1   Five metres.

QUESTION 2   a.   To show the safe limit that the bridge can carry.
              b.   Chieftain Mark 5 tank is Load Class 60.

QUESTION 3   a.   Close support bridging. Three to five minutes.
              b.   Deliberate support bridging. One to two hours.
              c.   Line of communication bridging. Days.

QUESTION 4   The criteria for the design of the Bailey bridge were:

              a.   Components easily handled.
              b.   Readily carried on standard vehicles.
              c.   Provide flexibility in design.
              d.   Capable of being built by non-specialists.
              e.   Small subsequent maintenance.

QUESTION 5   Close support bridges can be used in tandem to increase the gap-crossing capabilities.

QUESTION 6   Dry support bridges can be adapted to give greater gap-crossing capability by the use of piers or by increasing the strength of the bridge in bending.

QUESTION 7   The major advantages of floating bridges are:

              a.   Flexibility.
              b.   Comparatively cheap.

QUESTION 8   The slow traffic rate.

QUESTION 9   British policy is not to require an amphibious capability except
              for an engineer pathfinder.

QUESTION 10   Lines of communication bridges can utilise obsolete deliberate
              dry support bridging equipment.

TABLE 1 - MASS, WEIGHT, POWER

Vehicle	Mass (t)	Weight (kN)	NGP (kPa)	NGP (lb/in^2)	Engine Power (kW)	Engine Power (bhp)	Power to Mass kW/t	Power to Mass bhp/ton
Centurion Mk 13	51.8	508	91.6	13.3	485	690	9.4	12.7
Chieftain Mk 2	52.0	510	88.2	12.8	485	650	9.3	12.7
Chieftain Mk 5	55.0	539	93.5	13.6	537	720	9.8	13.3
Vickers Mk 3	38.4	379	87.0	12.4	485	676	12.6	17.1
XM1 GEN ABRAMS	55.0	540	90.4	13.1	1120	1500	21.3	28.5
M60 A1	48.0	471	76.5	11.1	560	750	11.7	15.9
M60 A2	51.0	500	74.4	10.8	560	750	11.0	14.9
Leopard 1	40.1	393	84.0	12.2	610	818	15.2	20.7
Leopard 2	55.0	540	83.0	12.1	1100	1475	20.0	27.0
T 55	36.6	359	79.0	11.5	433	580	11.8	16.1
T 62	37.0	363	79.0	11.5	433	580	11.7	15.9
T 72	41.0	404	87.0	12.6	582	780	14.2	19.0
T 10M	50.8	498	69.0	10.0	522	700	10.3	14.0
AMX 30	36.0	353	76.0	11.2	537	720	14.9	20.3
Merkava	56.0	548	-	-	671	900	12.0	16.1
S tank	37.6	369	88.0	12.8	K60:179 Boeing:365	240 490	9.7	13.2
Scorpion	7.9	77	34.5	5.0	145	195	18.4	25.1
Sheridan (US)	15.8	155	47.2	6.8	224	300	14.2	19.3
PT 76 (USSR)	14.0	137	47.0	6.8	179	240	12.8	17.4
M 114 A1 (US)	6.9	68	29.6	4.3	119	160	17.2	23.6
LYNX (US/Canada)	8.6	84	47.5	6.9	160	215	18.6	25.4
FV 432 Mk 2	15.0	147	77.0	11.2	179	240	11.9	16.3
M 113 (US)	11.0	107	51.6	7.5	160	215	14.5	19.9
Marder (FRG)	28.7	281	78.0	11.3	441	590	15.4	20.9
BMP (USSR)	14.0	137	50.0	7.1	210	280	15.0	20.0
PBV 302 (Sweden)	13.5	132	58.0	8.4	202	270	15.0	20.3

VEHICLES NOT YET IN SERVICE

Vehicle	Mass (t)	Weight (kN)	NGP (kPa)	NGP (lb/in^2)	Engine Power (kW)	Engine Power (bhp)	Power to Mass kW/t	Power to Mass bhp/ton
CHALLENGER I	60.0	589	98.0	14.2	895	1200	14.9	20.0
VICKERS VALIANT	43.6	430	79.5	11.5	RR 746 GM 471	1000 900	17.0 15.4	22.9 20.1

TABLE II – DIMENSIONS AND RATIOS

Length (Hull) (m)	Width (m)	Height (m)	Ground Clearance (m)	L/C ratio	Pitch ratio	Vehicle
7.82	3.39	2.97	0.508	1.70	1.73	Centurion Mk 13
7.47	3.50	2.82	0.508	1.75	1.68	Chieftain Mk 2
7.52	3.50	2.90	0.508	1.75	1.68	Chieftain Mk 5
7.56	3.23	2.71	0.41	1.69	1.77	Vickers Mk 3
7.77	3.58	2.64	0.48	1.61	1.73	XM1 GEN ABRAMS
6.93	3.63	3.28	0.453	1.42	1.75	M60 A1
6.91	3.58	3.20	0.463	1.44	1.75	M60 A2
7.00	3.25	2.36	0.46	1.56	1.66	Leopard 1
7.40	3.70	2.79	0.50	1.78	1.50	Leopard 2
6.20	3.27	2.35	0.58	1.45	1.6	T 55
6.81	3.30	2.31	0.58	1.61	1.48	T 62
6.40	3.38	2.27	0.46	1.46	1.60	T 72
7.3	3.56	2.41	0.668	1.75	1.54	T 10M
6.80	3.10	2.87	0.58	1.60	1.63	AMX 30
–	3.70	2.75	–	–	–	Merkava
6.90	3.30	2.08	2.54	1.10	2.20	S tank
4.39	2.18	2.096	0.36	1.70	1.52	Scorpion
6.30	2.79	2.95	0.483	1.50	1.78	Sheridan (US)
7.63	3.14	2.26	0.37	1.45	1.69	PT 76 (USSR)
4.47	2.33	2.15	0.36	1.43	1.63	M 114 A1 (US)
4.60	2.41	2.11	0.40	1.20	1.93	LYNX (US/CANADA)
5.11	2.97	1.88	0.406	1.28	1.80	FV 432 Mk 2
4.87	2.69	2.03	0.406	1.20	1.80	M 113 (US)
6.79	3.24	2.86	0.43	1.60	1.55	Marder (FRG)
6.52	3.02	1.92	0.40	1.41	1.82	BMP (USSR)
5.45	2.84	2.41	0.40	1.24	1.70	PBV 302 (Sweden)

VEHICLES NOT YET IN SERVICE

Length (Hull) (m)	Width (m)	Height (m)	Ground Clearance (m)	L/C ratio	Pitch ratio	Vehicle
8.39	3.51	2.89	0.50	1.79	1.69	CHALLENGER I
7.81	3.64	3.24	0.46	1.72	1.68	VICKERS VALIANT

TABLE III – CAPACITIES, ETC

Vehicle	Road speed (km/h)	Road range (km)	Fuel (1)	Main armament (mm)	No of rounds	No of rounds (secondary)	Crew
Centurion Mk 13	35	190	1036	105	64	3500 × .30 in	4
Chieftain Mk 2	40	370–400	886	120	53	6000 × 7.62 mm	4
Chieftain Mk 5	48	400–500	955	120	53	6000 × 7.62 mm	4
Vickers Mk 3	53	600	1000	105	44	4500 × .30 in	4
XM1 GEN ABRAMS	72	470	2000	105	55	10000 × 7.62 mm 1000 × .50 in	4
M60 A1	48	500	1365	105	63)	5950 × 7.62 mm	4
M60 A2	51	480	1365	152	13(+33)	1050 × .50 in	4
Leopard 1	65	600	1000	105	60	4800 × 7.62 mm	4
Leopard 2	68	500	1100	120	42	2000 × 7.62 mm	4
T 55	50	–	–	100	40–44	? × 7.62 mm	4
T 62	50	500	–	115	40–44	? × 7.62 mm	4
T 72	80	500	–	125	40	? × 7.62 mm	3
T 10M	50	240	1180	122	30	744 × 14.5 mm	4
AMX 30	65	500	1090	105	50	1000 × 12.7 mm 3000 × 7.62 mm	4
Merkava	50	–	–	105	62(?)	2000 × 7.62 mm	4
S tank	50	340	750	105	50	1500 × 7.62 mm	3
Scorpion	87	560	390	76	40	3000 × 7.62 mm	3
Sheridan (US)	70	600	614	152	29	3000 × 7.62 mm 1000 × 0.50 in	4
PT 76 (USSR)	44	250	–	76	40	? × 7.62 mm	3
M 114 A1 (US)	57	480	416	–	–	1000 × 0.50 in	3 or 4
LYNX (US/Canada)	70	512	364	–	–	1155 × 0.50 in 2000 × 0.30 in	3
FV 432 Mk 2	51	480	455	30		2000 × 7.62 mm	2+10
M 113 (US)	64	320	322	–	–	3000 × 0.52 in	2+11
Marder (FRG)	70	570	680	20	1240	5000 × 7.62 mm	2+8
BMP (USSR)	80	500	450	73	40	5 × Sagger	3+8
PBV 302 (Sweden)	60	300	285	20	–	–	2+10

VEHICLES NOT YET IN SERVICE

Vehicle	Road speed (km/h)	Road range (km)	Fuel (1)	Main armament (mm)	No of rounds	No of rounds (secondary)	Crew
CHALLENGER I	56	4–500(?)	1000 (?)	120	52	4000 × 7.62 mm	4
VICKERS VALIANT	59	600	1000 (?)	105 (120)	60 (44)	? × 7.62 mm × 0.5 in	4

Index

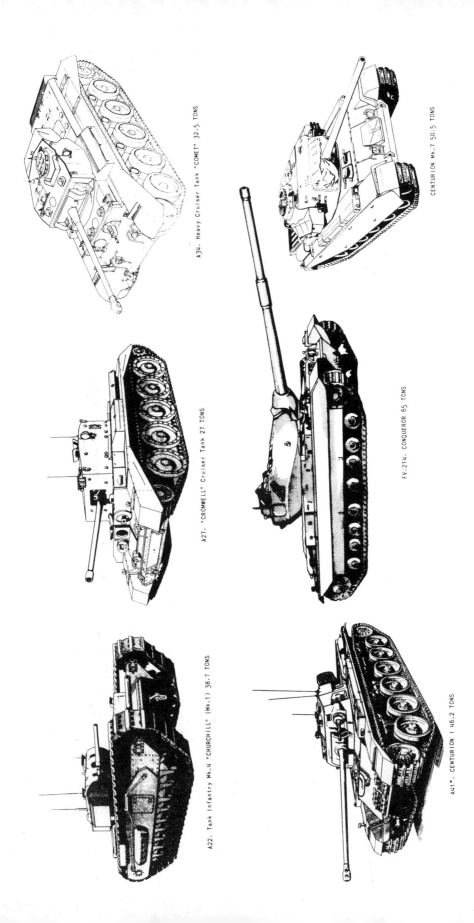

A34. Heavy Cruiser Tank "COMET" 32.5 TONS

CENTURION Mk.7 50.5 TONS

A27. "CROMWELL" Cruiser Tank 27 TONS

FV.214. CONQUEROR 65 TONS

A22. Tank Infantry Mk.4 "CHURCHILL" (Mk.1) 38.7 TONS

A41*. CENTURION I 46.2 TONS